Construction Health and Safety Manual

**Carpentry
Drywall
Acoustic and Interior Systems
Resilient Flooring**

**Construction Safety Association of Ontario
74 Victoria Street
Toronto, Ontario
M5C 2A5
(416) 366-1501   Fax: (416) 366-0232**

Developed by trade labour-management health and safety committees, this manual is fully a document of accord between labour and management authorities.

In the past, members of the public have used printed information that was outdated by subsequent improvements in knowledge and technology. We therefore make the following statement for their protection in future.

The information presented here is, to the best of our knowledge, current at time of printing and is intended for general application. This publication is not a definitive guide to government regulations or to practices and procedures wholly applicable under every circumstance. The appropriate regulations and statutes should be consulted. Although the Construction Safety Association of Ontario cannot guarantee the accuracy of, nor assume liability for, the information presented here, we are pleased to answer individual requests for counselling and advice.

Labour-Management

The Construction Safety Association of Ontario thanks the members of the Labour-Management Health and Safety Committees who contributed their knowledge, experience, and time in preparing this manual.

- The Carpenters' Trade Labour-Management Health and Safety Committee

- The Acoustical, Drywall, & Interior Systems Trade Labour-Management Health and Safety Committee

FOREWORD

Health and safety information in this manual is broadly divided into two categories.

Chapters I-17 cover topics of use and interest to all construction trades. The subjects include responsibilities for workplace health and safety; personal protective equipment; first aid and emergency procedures; back care; housekeeping; and access equipment such as ladders, scaffolds, and elevating work platforms.

Health and safety subjects in chapters 18-26 are directed specifically to carpenters, drywallers, installers of acoustic and interior systems, and resilient floor layers.

Topics include hand and power tools for these trades and step-by-step guidelines for welding, cutting, and formwork.

CONTENTS

Procedures

1 RESPONSIBILITIES

General

The health and safety responsibilities of all parties on a construction project are specified in the current *Occupational Health and Safety Act* and *Regulations for Construction Projects*.

Responsibilities are prescribed in particular for constructor, employer, supervisor, and worker. Each party has specific responsibilities to meet on a construction project.

For more detailed information, consult the current Act and Regulations.

Remember — safety begins with you!

Emergency Procedures

1 TAKE COMMAND
Assign the following duties to specific personnel.

2 PROVIDE PROTECTION
Protect the accident scene from continuing or further hazards – for instance, traffic, operating machinery, fire or live wires.

3 GIVE FIRST AID
Give first aid to the injured as soon as possible. For basic first aid, see Chapter 13.

4 CALL AN AMBULANCE
Call an ambulance and any other emergency services required. In some locales, dialing 911 puts you in touch with all emergency services.

5 GUIDE THE AMBULANCE
Meet and direct the ambulance to the accident scene.

6 GET NAME OF HOSPITAL
For follow-up, find out where the injured is being taken.

7 ADVISE MANAGEMENT
Inform senior management. They can then contact relatives, notify authorities, and start procedures for reporting and investigating the accident.

8 ISOLATE THE ACCIDENT SCENE
Barricade, rope off or post a guard at the scene to make sure that nothing is moved or changed until authorities have completed their investigation.

Figure 1

Health and Safety Representative

The health and safety representative must be familiar with
- the current *Occupational Health and Safety Act* and *Regulations for Construction projects*
- procedures in the event of an emergency (Figure 1)
- procedures for refusal to work where health and safety are in danger (Figure 2).

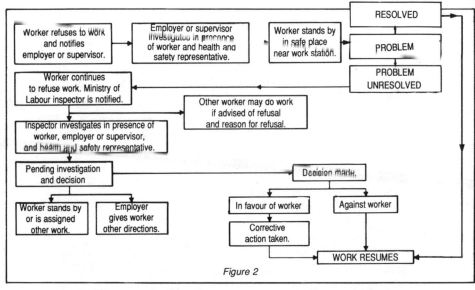

Figure 2

Accidents and Injuries

All accidents and injuries, regardless of severity, must be reported immediately.

Procedures for reporting accidents — and the type of accidents that must be reported — are spelled out in the *Occupational Health and Safety Act* and *Regulations for Construction Projects*.

Further information is available from the Ministry of Labour.

Certified Committee Members

Where a project regularly employs 50 or more workers, the health and safety committee on the project must have at least one member representing workers and one member representing the constructor who are certified by the Workplace Health and Safety Agency (Figure 3).

If no members of a health and safety committee are certified, the workers and constructor must each select one member of the committee to become certified.

A certified member who receives a complaint regarding a dangerous circumstance can investigate the complaint under the authority of the *Occupational Health and Safety Act*. The member may also ask a supervisor to investigate a situation where the member "has reason to believe" that a dangerous circumstance may exist.

The supervisor must investigate the situation promptly in the presence of the certified member.

The certified member may also request that another certified member representing the other party at the workplace investigate the situation if the first certified member "has reason to believe" that the dangerous circumstance still exists after the supervisor's investigation and remedial action, if any, has been taken.

The second certified member must promptly investigate the situation in the presence of the first certified member and, if both certified members agree, they may direct the constructor or employer to stop work or stop the use of any part of the workplace, including machines and other equipment. The constructor or employer must immediately comply with the order.

If both certified members do not agree that a dangerous circumstance exists, either may request that a Ministry of Labour inspector investigate the situation. The inspector must investigate and provide both members with a written report.

Ministry of Labour Inspectors

An inspector can visit a site at any time and exercise fairly broad powers to inspect, ask questions, and give orders. If the inspector approaches a worker directly, the worker must answer questions and cooperate. The supervisor must be informed of any orders given or recommendations made.

Health and Safety Representatives and Committee

Size and Duration of Project	Representative or Committee	Who Creates Committee	Number of Members	Membership Requirements
5 Workers or Less				
6-19 workers and more than 3 months or 6+ workers and less than 3 months	One Health and Safety Representative			
20-49 workers and more than 3 months	Joint Health and Safety Committee	Constructor	At least two	At least one non-management worker at the project **and** one management representative from the workplace if possible
50+ workers and more than 3 months	Joint Health and Safety Committee	Constructor	At least four	Half non-management workers from the workplace (with at least one "certified" in the future). Half management representatives from the project if possible (with at least one "certified" in the future).
	Worker Trades Committee	Health and Safety Committee	At least one worker representative from each trade	One worker representative from each trade

Requirements Under the Occupational Health and Safety Act

Selection of Members	Powers and Rights
Representative selected by workers or union(s)	• Obtain information from a constructor or employer regarding the testing of equipment, materials, or chemicals in the workplace. • Inspect the workplace at least once a month, with the full cooperation of constructor, employers, and workers. • Ask for and obtain information regarding existing or potential hazards in the workplace. • Make health and safety recommendations to a constructor or employer, who must respond in writing within 21 days, either giving a timetable for implementation or giving reasons for disagreeing with the recommendations. • Where a person has been killed or critically injured in the workplace, investigate the circumstances of the accident and report findings to a director of the Ministry of Labour. • Exercise all the powers granted to the health and safety representative by virtue of a collective agreement.
Worker representatives selected from the site by workers or trade union(s) represented. Management representatives selected by constructor or employer.	• Identify situations that may be a source of danger or hazard to workers. • Make recommendations regarding health and safety matters. • Recommend maintenance and monitoring programs. • Obtain information from constructors or employers regarding testing of equipment or environments and be present when testing is initiated.
Worker representatives selected from the site by workers or trade union(s) represented. Management representatives selected by constructor or employer.	
Members to be selected by trade workers or trade union(s) at the site. Members do not have to be workers at the site.	Advise the joint health and safety committee of the health and safety concerns of the workers in the trades at the workplace.

Figure 3

5

In some cases the health and safety representative, worker member of a health and safety committee, or worker selected by fellow workers or union has a right to take part in accident investigation.

The results of accident investigation and reporting should be made known to all personnel on site. Recommendations should be implemented to prevent the accident from happening again.

In all cases of injury, the **EMPLOYER** must do the following.
1. Make sure that first aid is given immediately, as required by law.
2. Record the first aid treatment or advice given to the worker.
3. Complete and give to the worker a Treatment Memorandum (Form 156) if health care is needed.
4. Provide immediate transportation to a hospital or a physician's office, if necessary.
5. Submit to the Workers Compensation Board, within three days of learning of an accident, an Employer's Report of an Accident/Injury Industrial Disease (Form 7) and any other information that may be required.
6. Pay full wages and benefits for the day or shift on which the injury occurred when compensation is payable for loss of earnings.
7. Notify the Ministry of Labour, health and safety representative and/or committee, and union as required by legislation.

The **WORKER** must do the following.
1. Promptly obtain first aid.
2. Notify the employer, foreman, supervisor, and worker safety representative immediately of an injury requiring health care and obtain from the employer a completed Treatment Memorandum (Form 156) to take to the physician or the hospital. Failure to report promptly can affect your benefits and subject your employer to fines.
3. Choose a physician or other qualified practitioner with the understanding that a change of physician cannot be made without permission of the WCB.
4. Complete and promptly return all report forms received from the WCB.

2 FIRST AID

Regulation 950 under the *Workers' Compensation Act* details the
obligations of employers regarding first aid equipment, facilities, and
trained personnel in all workplaces. Section 91/4 of the Act authorizes
the WCB to penalize employers who do not comply with these
requirements.

Basic first aid concentrates on **breathing, bleeding,** and **burns.**

Breathing

If the casualty is unconscious, check for breathing. Listen at the mouth
and nose. Watch and feel for chest movement.

If the casualty is not breathing, start artificial respiration immediately. The
most efficient method is mouth-to-mouth (Figure 4).

Bleeding

Control external bleeding immediately.

- Apply direct pressure to stop blood flow.
- Place casualty in comfortable position and elevate affected part.
- Rest to slow circulation.
- Apply direct pressure with hand over dressing.
- Do not remove blood-soaked dressing. Add another dressing and
  continue pressing.
- When bleeding is controlled, secure bandage and maintain elevation.

The simple formula for the control of bleeding is Rest, Elevate,
Direct Pressure. — R.E.D.

A deep wound in the palm of the hand usually results in severe bleeding.
You should control bleeding from a wound across the palm of the hand
with **direct pressure, elevation,** and **rest.**

- Make a fist and apply pressure to the wound; at the same time,
  elevate the hand.
- Seat the casualty.

First Aid – Breathing

If the injured person is not breathing, start artificial respiration immediately. The most efficient method is mouth-to-mouth.

- Check for breathing.
- Listen at the mouth and nose.
- Watch and feel for chest movement.

- Open the airway.
- Lift chin.
- Remove obvious foreign material.

- Pinch nostrils closed.
- Take a breath.

- Make a tight seal at the mouth.
- Blow two breaths.

- Watch for chest movement.
- If air is getting into the lungs, continue blowing at your normal breathing rate.
- For an adult, blow one breath every five seconds.
- For an infant or young child, make a tight seal over the mouth and nose and blow gentle puffs — one breath every three seconds.

Figure 4

8

- Place a wad of gauze dressings over the wound and close the fingers around the wad to maintain pressure.
- Elevate the hand again to a higher position.

For a crushed hand, the treatment is different.

1. Steady and support the injured hand.
2. Place a pad of dressings in the palm of the hand to keep it in the position of function.
3. Remove any jewellery before swelling occurs.
4. Transfer the hand to a padded splint extending from mid-forearm to fingertips and elevate slightly.
5. Place non-stick dressings between the fingers and between the index finger and thumb.
6. Cover the injured hand with sterile dressings or a clean cloth.
7. Starting at the fingertips, apply a roller bandage to secure the hand to the splint.
8. Apply an arm sling. Transport the casualty to medical aid.

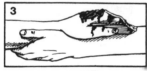

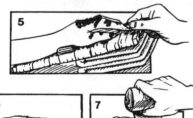

Courtesy St. John Ambulance

9

Burns

Immediately immerse the burned part in ice water or immediately apply ice or clean cloths soaked in cold water.

Cold will
- reduce the temperature of the burned area and prevent further damage
- reduce swelling and blistering
- relieve pain.

Medical Alert

Valuable information about the history of a casualty can often be found on a **Medical Alert** device — bracelet, necklace, or pocket card. This warning alerts first aiders and medical personnel to the fact that the casualty
- has a medical condition requiring special treatment
    or
- is **allergic** to certain substances.

Severed Tissue

Completely or partially severed parts must be preserved, regardless of their condition, and taken to the medical facility with the casualty.

Bagging of completely severed part

Partially severed part should be
- kept as near as possible to its normal position
- covered with sterile gauze dressing, bandaged, and supported
- kept cool with an ice bag or cold compress outside the bandage.

Completely severed part should be
- wrapped in sterile gauze moistened with clean water, placed in a clean watertight plastic bag and sealed, and a record made of the time this was done
- placed in another plastic bag or container partially filled with crushed ice
- transported with the casualty to a medical facility.

Do not attempt to clean severed parts and do not use antiseptic solutions.

If possible, notify medical facility that casualty is being transported with partially or completely severed parts.

Heat and Cold Exposures

Workers required to work in high temperatures or cold environments must take precautions against exposure.

A healthy worker acclimatizes to this exposure and can maintain a normal temperature by conserving heat in the cold and by dissipating heat when it is hot.

When a body sweats excessively to dissipate heat, the resulting loss of body salts and fluids causes a muscular reaction called heat cramps. Prolonged exposure to a hot environment causes heat exhaustion. When the temperature control mechanisms of the body fail, heat stroke results and the person may die.

Heat Exhaustion

Symptoms
- Pulse weak and rapid
- Breathing rapid and shallow
- Vision blurred
- Skin cold and clammy
- Nausea and vomiting.

Treatment
- Move out of the heat.
- Place at rest.
- Loosen tight clothing.
- Keep head low, raise legs and feet slightly.
- For cramps, give a glass of slightly salted water (add 1/4 teaspoon salt). Give as much as the casualty will take.
- Watch breathing; get medical help.

Heat Stroke

Symptoms
- Temperature of 42C to 44C
- Pulse rapid and progressively weaker
- Breathing noisy
- Often no perspiration in cases of non-exhaustion heat stroke
- Nausea and vomiting.

Treatment
- Sponge with cold water.
- Cover with wet sheets.
- Direct current of air around casualty by hand or electric fan.
- Obtain prompt medical aid.

Cold Exposure

Exposure to cold can injure the surface of the body causing local tissue damage. It can also cause general body-cooling that can be fatal. Contributing factors include
- temperature
- wind velocity
- worker's age and physical condition
- degree of protection from outer clothing or covering
- exposure to cold or icy water.

A body exposed to dangerously low temperatures can suffer injuries such as hypothermia and frostbite.

Stay Warm
- Wear clothing that will maintain body heat without sweating. Several layers of light, loose-fitting clothing trap air and have greater protective value than one layer of heavy clothing.
- Cover your head. A warm hat liner is ideal for keeping your head and ears warm.
- Avoid tight-fitting boots. When practical, change boots regularly to allow each pair to dry completely. This will keep your feet a lot dryer and warmer.

- Wear mittens instead of gloves when practical. This will keep your hands a lot warmer.

Stay Dry
- Avoid wetness due to sweating, rain, or snow. Wetness contributes to heat loss.

Stay Safe
- Limit the length of time you spend in extreme cold conditions.
- Have someone check you for signs of frostbite.

Avoid Fatigue
- Rest periodically in a sheltered location.

Avoid Tobacco
- Nicotine decreases blood flow and increases the possibility of cold injury.

Avoid Alcohol
- Because it dilates the blood vessels, alcohol causes additional heat loss.

Frostbite — Skin looks white, waxy, and feels numb. Freezing causes hardening.

- Warm frostbitten area gradually with body heat. **Do not rub.**
- Do not thaw hands or feet unless medical aid is far away and there is no chance of refreezing. Parts are better thawed in a hospital.
- If there are blisters, apply sterile dressings and bandage lightly to prevent breaking. Get medical attention.

Hypothermia

Caused when body temperature falls below normal during prolonged exposure to cold, it can develop quickly and be fatal.

Danger signs are shivering, slurred speech, stumbling, and drowsiness.

Condition is severe when shivering stops. Unconsciousness and stopped breathing may follow.

First aid for hypothermia must
- stop further cooling of the body
- provide heat to begin rewarming.

Treatment
- Remove casualty carefully to shelter. Movement or rough handling can upset heart rhythm.
- Keep the casualty awake.
- Remove wet clothing and wrap casualty in warm covers.
- Rewarm neck, chest, abdomen, and groin — but not extremities.
- Apply direct body heat or safe heating devices.
- Give warm, sweet drinks, if casualty is conscious.
- Monitor breathing, give artificial respiration if needed.
- Call for medical aid or transport carefully to nearest facility.

Immersion Foot — Caused by wet cooling of the feet, over an extended period, at temperatures above freezing. It is most prevalent in persons who spend long periods with their feet in cold water or mud.

Immersion foot can be prevented by keeping the feet dry. Carry spare socks in a warm place, such as inside the jacket, and change them often to help prevent this condition.

Initially the feet are cold, swollen, and waxy, and may be numb. After warming, they may become red, swollen, and hot, and blisters may occur.

14

In advanced stages of immersion foot, gangrene may develop.

- Remove wet footwear and warm cold areas.
- Get medical aid.

Embedded Object

Do not attempt to pull out objects embedded in a wound. Pulling nails, splinters, or pieces of glass from wound will cause more damage and will increase bleeding.

- Cover lightly with dressing without pressure on the object.
- Apply pressure around the wound and away from the embedded object.
- Get medical help as soon as possible.

Eye Injuries

Do not attempt to remove particles on the pupil or stuck to the eyeball.

- Remove loose particles with care using the moistened corner of a tissue.
- If that fails, cover the eye lightly with a dressing to prevent movement and transport to a medical facility.
- Avoid rubbing the injured eye and causing further injury.

Unconsciousness

Loss of consciousness may threaten life if the casualty is face-up and the tongue has dropped to the back of the throat, blocking the airway.

- Make certain that the person is breathing before looking for the cause of unconsciousness.
- If injuries permit, place the casualty in the recovery position (Figure 5) with the neck extended.
- Never give anything by mouth to an unconscious casualty.

Fractures

A fracture is a break or a crack in a bone.

- Steady and support the injury. **Do not move the victim.**
- Dress the wound and control any bleeding.
- If casualty must be moved for safety, secure the limb with padded splints.
- Check for pulse. If none, get medical aid immediately.
- Reassure and keep warm to prevent shock until help arrives.

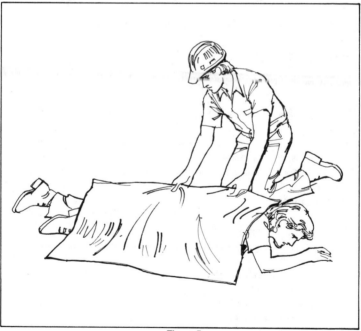

Figure 5

Frequently construction trades are required to work with new hazardous materials or previously installed hazardous materials requiring repair, maintenance, or removal. Some materials used for many years and thought harmless are now identified as hazardous.

Proper handling requires careful planning, training, and use of personal protective equipment or controls.

Some hazardous materials common in construction are
- compressed gas (acetylene, nitrogen, oxygen)
- flammable and combustible materials (solvents)
- oxidizing materials (epoxy hardeners)
- solvents, coatings, and sealers
- asbestos and silica
- acids and alkalis.

Right to Know

> The Workplace Hazardous Materials Information System (WHMIS) gives everyone the right to know about the hazards of materials they work with and provides the means to find out that information. It does this through
> - labels
> - material safety data sheets
> - worker training and education.

All employers are required by law to provide WHMIS training for specific controlled products the worker will be working with or near. Training should be provided as new products are introduced with a general updating on new products at least annually.

Controlled products under WHMIS include six classes, identified by appropriate symbols (Figure 6).

The requirements for supplier and workplace labels are shown in Figure 7.

CLASS	SYMBOL	EXAMPLE
Class A: Compressed Gas		oxygen
Class B: Flammable and Combustible Material		acetone
Class C: Oxidizing Material		chromic acid
Class D: Poisonous and Infectious Material		
1. Materials causing immediate and serious toxic effects		ammonia
2. Materials causing other toxic effects		asbestos
3. Biohazardous Infectious Material		contaminated blood products
Class E: Corrosive Material		hydrochloric acid sodium hydroxide
Class F: Dangerously Reactive Material		acetylene

Figure 6

Supplier labels are required on controlled products with a volume of more than 100 millilitres and must include

- product identifier
- appropriate hazard symbol(s)
- risk phrases (such as "dangerous if inhaled")
- precautions (such as "wear rubber gloves")
- first aid measures
- supplier identifier
- statement that a material safety data sheet (MSDS) is available for the product.

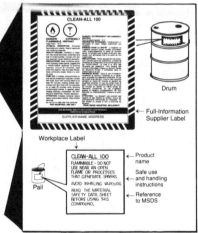

Figure 7

Workplace labels are required when controlled products are produced onsite or have been transferred from a supplier-labelled container to a different container. Workplace labels must include

- product identifier
- safe handling instructions
- statement that an MSDS is available for the product.

If details on the ingredients, health effects, handling, and other aspects
of a hazardous product are not available from suppliers or employers,
call the Construction Safety Association of Ontario at 1-800-387-0847
and provide the following information.

- Product name (for example, Solvex 100)
- Manufacturer's name and place of manufacture (for example, ABC
  Chemical, Montreal, Quebec)
- What is the product being used for? (for example, to clean parts)
- How is it being used? (for example, sprayed on)
- Is it being mixed with something else?
- Is it being heated?
- In what area is it being used? (for example, outdoors or in a holding
  tank)
- What does the label say?
- How can information be conveyed to you?

Designated Substances

"Designated substances" are substances that have been targeted for
special regulation by the Ministry of Labour. Generally these substances
are well-known toxic materials which present serious risk of illness.

Designated substances encountered in construction include asbestos,
lead, coal tar products, and silica. If any designated substances are
present where construction, maintenance, or renovation is planned, the
parties involved must be notified and informed.

The *Occupational Health and Safety Act* requires that owners notify
contractors of the presence of any designated substances. Contractors
also have a responsibility to advise subcontractors. This notification must
take place before binding contracts are arranged.

For more information on designated substances, contact the Ministry of
Labour.

4 BACK CARE

Nearly 25 % of the lost-time injuries in construction are related to the back. More than half of these injuries result from lifting excessive weight or lifting incorrectly.

To prevent injuries, three factors are necessary:

1. proper posture
2. correct lifting techniques
3. regular exercise.

Posture

Correct posture is not an erect, military pose. It means maintaining the naturally occurring curves in your spine.

You have two inward curves — at the neck and low back — and one outward curve — at the upper back.

Keeping your spine aligned in this manner reduces everyday stresses on your back and minimizes the effects of the normal aging process on the spine.

When working in a crouched, bent, or stooping position for a prolonged period, take regular breaks by standing up and bending backwards three times.

Correct Posture

Cervical Lordosis

Thoracic Kyphosis

Lumbar Lordosis

You have two inward curves (lordosis), one each at the neck and low back, and one outward curve (kyphosis) at the upper back.

Normal

Prolonged standing often causes an increased curve in your back. Elevating one foot on a stool or any other object (a phone book or brick will do) will take stress off the lower spine.

Sway Back

An increased curve in your lower back will jam the vertabrae together (sway back). If held too long, the position will cause lower back muscle and ligaments to tighten and lead to lower back pain.

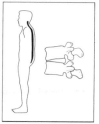

Flat Back

Too little curve (flat back) will put extra pressure on the front of your discs. This may contribute to disc problems and pain.

Work Overhead

When working overhead in an arched position for prolonged periods, take regular breaks by returning to stable footing and bending forward three times.

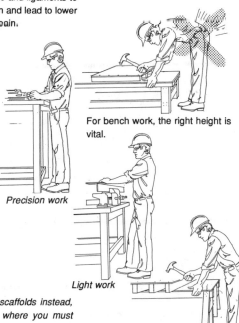

For bench work, the right height is vital.

Precision work

Light work

If possible avoid working on ladders. Use scaffolds instead, especially for long-term tasks or for jobs where you must handle heavy materials.

Heavy work

Materials Handling

Proper Lifting

1. Plan your move.
   - Size up the load and make sure pathway is clear.
   - Get help as needed.
   - Use a dolly or other device if necessary.

2. Use a wide-balanced stance with one foot slightly ahead of the other.

3. Get as close to the load as possible.

4. Tighten your stomach muscles as the lift begins.

5. When lifting, keep your lower back in its normal arched position and use your legs to lift.

6. Pick up your feet and pivot to turn — don't twist your back.

7. Lower the load slowly, maintaining the curve in your lower back.

Your back can manage most lifts — if you lift correctly.

Avoid lifting above shoulder height. This causes the back to arch, placing heavy stress on the small joints of the spine.

Do not catch falling objects. Your muscles may not have time to coordinate properly to protect the spine.

Push rather than pull. Pushing allows you to maintain the normal curves in your back.

Weight Transfer

Pull the object toward you while transferring your weight to the lift side.

Lift only to the level required.

Shift your weight to your other leg while pushing the object into position.

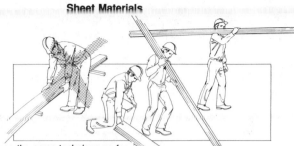

If sheets are on the floor, use the same technique as for lifting long lumber. Lift one end first.

When you handle sheet materials, use proper techniques to protect your back.

Where possible, store sheets at a convenient height and above ground on timbers or trestles.

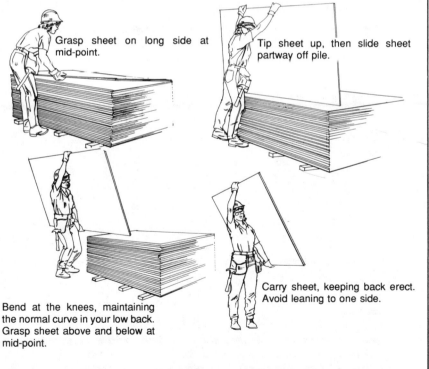

Grasp sheet on long side at mid-point.

Tip sheet up, then slide sheet partway off pile.

Bend at the knees, maintaining the normal curve in your low back. Grasp sheet above and below at mid-point.

Carry sheet, keeping back erect. Avoid leaning to one side.

For long carries, use carrying handles. Better yet, if surface is smooth and hard use a drywall cart.

Two-Person Lift

Lifters should be of similar height. Before starting they should decide on lifting strategy and who will take charge.

For a two-person lift of a long load, the lifter who takes charge must see that the load is carried on the same side, with a clear line of vision. Begin by lifting load from ground to waist height. Then lift the load from waist to shoulder.

Carrying on Stairs

Use your stomach muscles to help support and protect your back. If possible, the tallest and/or strongest person should be at the bottom of the load.

Balance

Avoid one-handed carrying if possible. Try to distribute the weight evenly on each side. If you can't avoid one-handed carrying, such as with a single pail, hold the free arm either straight out or on your hip as a counterbalance.

Mechanical Help

Use a cart or dolly for transporting tools and equipment wherever possible.

Consider using pallets where surface conditions allow.

Wheelbarrows with dual wheels are a great improvement over single wheels. Better balance and increased flotation over soft ground make wheeling easier on the back.

Lift tables with casters for heavy components can be helpful. These tables are light, carry loads of several hundred pounds, and have adjustable heights from one to several feet.

Rolling frame scaffolds with a few tube-and-clamp components may be useful for moving heavy objects.

A small rolling scaffold can be used to provide access or to transport tools and materials.

Hoisting a heavy load on a rope is hard work, but the pulley principle (block and tackle) makes it easier.

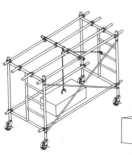

Rolling frame scaffolds with a few tube-and-clamp components may be useful for moving heavy objects such as motors or drives where other devices such as forklifts are not available.

Scaffold frames with tube-and-clamp components, casters, and a small boat winch have many uses in moving and lifting components weighing 100 to 200 pounds.

A small rolling scaffold can be used to provide access or to transport tools and materials.

Exercise

Construction work strengthens some muscles while others become shorter and weaker, creating a muscle imbalance. A regular exercise program can help to prevent this from happening.

A good exercise program should consist of four basic parts:
1. warm-up
2. main workout
0. strength and stretch
4. cool-down.

Warm-Up

This is a general exercise program only. Before starting any exercise program, consult your doctor first.

If you have any concerns or experience any pain while doing the exercises, stop and consult your doctor.

1. March in Place
Start: Stand in position.

Action: Alternately raise knees. Swing arms and hands in alternating opposite direction. Make sure that heels contact the ground.

2. Arm Circles
Start: Stand with arms raised horizontally, palms down, and feet shoulder-width apart.

Action: Rotate arms in forward circular motion for 15 seconds. Repeat in opposite direction for 15 seconds.

Stretching Program

The following stretching exercises are of greatest value before work starts. They may, however, be done at any convenient time. Whenever they are done, a brief warm-up (walking briskly or jogging on the spot) is most beneficial.

The exercises should be performed in a slow, controlled manner and held in a sustained stretch. Avoid bouncy, jerky movements which may tear muscle fibres.

3. Knee to Chest
Start: Support yourself securely with one hand.

Action: Pull your knee toward your chest and grasp around your knee with your free hand. Hold the stretch for 30 seconds. Lower your leg to the ground and repeat with the other leg. Repeat three times for each leg.

4. Hip Stretch
Start: Stand with one foot in front of the other. Place hands above the knee of the front leg.

Action: Gently bend front knee, keeping back foot flat on the floor. Hold 20-30 seconds. Repeat with other leg. Repeat three times for each leg.

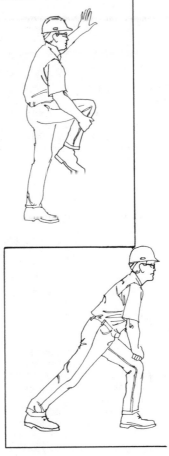

5. Thigh Stretch

Start: Support yourself with one hand on something secure.

Action: Bend your knee back and grasp your ankle with your free hand. Gently pull your ankle towards your body, keeping your trunk straight. Hold 20 to 30 seconds then repeat with other leg. Repeat three times for each leg.

6. Calf Stretch

Start: Stand slightly away from a solid support and lean on it with your outstretched hands. Bend the forward leg and place the other leg straight behind you.

Action: Slowly move your hips forward, keeping the heel of the back leg on the ground. Hold 30 seconds, relax, and repeat with other leg. Repeat three times for each leg.

7. Hamstring Stretch

Start: Place the back of your heel on a platform at a comfortable height. Bend your supporting leg slightly.

Action: Looking straight ahead, slowly bend forward at the hips until you feel a good stretch at the back of the raised leg. Hold 30 seconds and repeat with other leg. Repeat three times for each leg.

5 HOUSEKEEPING

Many injuries result from poor housekeeping. Improper storage of materials and cluttered work areas are not safe. To maintain a clean, hazard-free workplace, all groups — management, supervision, and workers — must cooperate.

General

Regulations for safe housekeeping require
- daily jobsite cleanup program
- disposal of rubbish
- individual cleanup duties for all workers
- materials piled, stacked, or otherwise stored to prevent tipping and collapsing
- materials stored away from overhead powerlines
- work and travel areas kept tidy, well-lit, and ventilated (Figure 8)
- signs posted to warn workers of hazardous areas.

The basics of good housekeeping are shown in Figure 9.

Specific

- Gather up and remove debris as often as required to keep work and travel areas orderly.
- Keep equipment and the areas around equipment clear of scrap and waste.
- Keep stairways, passageways, and gangways free of material, supplies and obstructions at all times.
- Secure loose or light material stored on roof or on open floors to prevent blowing by wind.
- Pick up, store, or dispose of tools, material, or debris which may cause tripping or other hazards.
- Before handling used lumber, remove or bend over protruding nails and chip away hardened concrete.
- Wear eye protection when there is any risk of eye injury.
- Do not permit rubbish to fall freely from any level of the project. Lower by means of chute or other approved devices (Figure 10).
- Do not throw materials or tools from one level to another.

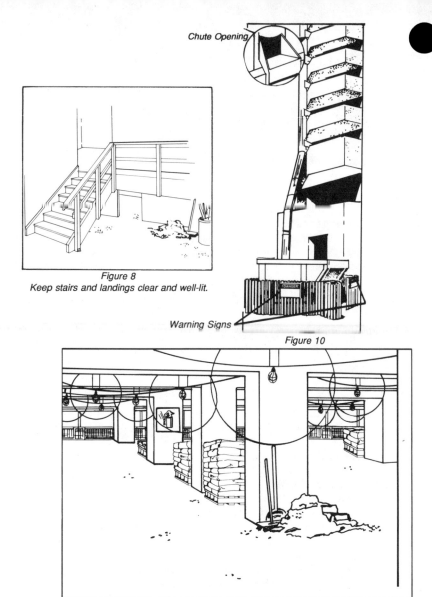

Chute Opening

Figure 8
Keep stairs and landings clear and well-lit.

Warning Signs

Figure 10

Figure 9
Good housekeeping means clear traffic and work areas, out-of-the-way storage, adequate illumination, and cleanup of debris.

Figure 11

Figure 12
Secure material against the wind. After removing material, resecure pile.

31

- Do not lower or raise any tool or equipment by its own cord or supply hose.

- When guardrails must be removed to land, unload, or handle material, wear fall-arrest equipment (Figure 11). The area must also be roped off with warning signs posted.

In shops it is relatively easy to maintain a clean work area. Barriers and warning lines can also be set up to isolate table saws and other equipment.

On construction sites, arrangements are more difficult. Equipment often sits in basements, on decks, or in corners with insufficient working space and sometimes open to the weather. The footing may simply consist of a piece of plywood.

Around table saws and similar equipment, keep the immediate area clear of scrap to avoid tripping hazards and provide sound footing.

Airborne wood dust can be a respiratory hazard, causing problems ranging from simple irritation of the eyes, nose, and throat to more serious health effects. Dust collectors should be installed in shops to remove sawdust from air and equipment. Wood dust is also very flammable.

In construction, saws and other tools are often operated in the open air where dust presents no hazard. However, dust masks or respirators should be worn whenever ventilation is inadequate.

Storage

Storage areas should be at least 1.8 metres (6 feet) from roof or floor openings, excavations, or any open edges where material may fall off (Figure 12).

Near openings, arrange material so that it cannot roll or slide in the direction of the opening.

Flammable Materials

- Use copper grounding straps to keep static electricity from building up in containers, racks, flooring, and other surfaces (Figure 13).

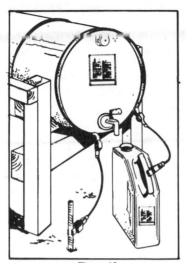

Figure 13
Dispensing and receiving containers should both be grounded.

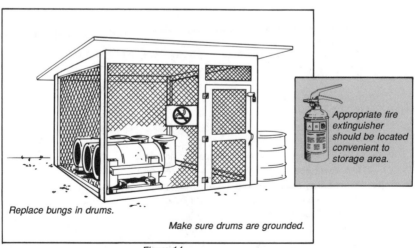

Appropriate fire extinguisher should be located convenient to storage area.

Replace bungs in drums.

Make sure drums are grounded.

Figure 14
Storage of Flammable Liquids

- Store fuel only in containers approved by the Canadian Standards Association (CSA) or Underwriters' Laboratories of Canada (ULC).
- Ensure that electric fixtures and switches are explosion-proof where flammable materials are stored.
- See Figure 14 for pointers on safe storage.

Hazardous Chemicals

- Refer to material safety data sheets (MSDSs) for specific information on each product.
- Follow manufacturer's recommendations for storage.
- Observe all restrictions concerning heat, moisture, vibration, impact, sparks, and safe working distance.
- Post warning signs where required.
- Have equipment ready to clean up spills quickly.
- For special handling and disposal later, store empty containers in secure area away from full containers.

Bags and Sacks

- Do not pile bagged material more than 10 bags high unless the face of the pile is supported by the walls of a storage bin or enclosure.
- Do not move piles more than 10 bags high unless fully banded or wrapped.
- Cross-pile bags and sacks for added stability. Pile only to a safe and convenient height for loading and unloading.

Compressed Gas Cylinders

- Store and move cylinders in the upright position. Secure cylinders upright with chains or rope.
- Lock up cylinders to prevent vandalism and theft.
- Wherever possible, store cylinders in a secure area **outdoors.**
- Keep full cylinders apart from empty cylinders.
- Store cylinders of different gases separately.
- Keep cylinders away from heat sources.
- When heating with propane, keep 45-kilogram (100 lb.) cylinders at least 4.5 metres (15 feet) away from heaters; keep large tanks at least 7.6 metres (25 feet) away.

Lumber

- Stack on level sills.
- Stack reusable lumber according to size and length. Remove nails during stacking.
- Support lumber at every 1.3-metre (4-foot) span.
- Cross-pile or cross-strip when the pile will be more than 1.3 metres (4 feet) high.

Fire Protection

Housekeeping includes fire prevention and fire protection. Workers must be trained to use fire extinguishers properly.

Fire extinguishers must be
- accessible
- regularly inspected
- promptly refilled after use.

Extinguishers must be provided
- where flammable materials are stored, handled, or used
- where temporary oil- or gas-fired equipment is being used
- where welding or open-flame cutting is being done
- on each storey of an enclosed building being constructed or renovated
- in shops for at least every 300 square metres of floor area.

Fire extinguishers are classified according to their capacity to fight specific types of fires (Figure 15).

Don't wait for a fire before learning how to operate the extinguisher in your work area.

For most operations, a 4A40BC extinguisher is adequate.

Extinguishers have a very short duration of discharge — usually less than 60 seconds. Be sure to aim at the base of the fire.

Class "A" Extinguishers

For fires in ordinary combustible materials such as wood, paper and textiles where a quenching, cooling effect is required.

Class "B" Extinguishers

For flammable liquid and gas fires, such as oil, gasoline, paint and grease where oxygen exclusion or flame interruption is essential.

Class "C" Extinguishers

For fires involving electrical wiring and equipment where the non-conductivity of the extinguishing agent is crucial.

This type of extinguisher should be present wherever functional testing and system energizing take place.

Class "D" Extinguishers

For fires in combustible metals such as sodium, magnesium and potassium.

How to Use the Extinguisher

Aim the extinguisher at the base of the fire to extinguish the flames at their source.

Figure 15

36

Equipment

6 PERSONAL PROTECTIVE EQUIPMENT

General

The following are the minimum recommended requirements for personal protection.

- For your personal safety on the job do not wear
  - loose clothing or cuffs
  - greasy or oily clothing, gloves, or boots
  - torn or ragged clothing
  - finger rings.

- Neck chains are hazardous and must be worn under clothing so that they don't hang out. Long hair must be tied back or otherwise confined.

- Clothing made of synthetic fibres can be readily ignited and melted by electric flash. Cotton or wool fabrics are more flame-retardant and therefore recommended.

Head Protection

- Construction workers must obtain and wear, at all times on the job, a Canadian Standards (CSA) certified Class B safety hat (Figure 16).

- Safety hats must not be painted.

- The shell and suspension of safety hats must be inspected regularly and replaced if cracks, deep scratches, or other defects are detected.

Foot Protection

- At all times on the job, construction workers must wear CSA-certified Grade 1 footwear. Such boots bear a green triangular patch stamped with the CSA registered trademark on the outside and a rectangular green label on the inside (Figure 17).

Table 1: Classification of Hazards and Recommended Protectors

ACTIVITIES	SPECTACLES WITH SIDE SHIELDS Clear (C) / Radiation (R)	EYECUP GOGGLES Impact (I) / Dust & Splash (D&S) / Radiation (R)	COVER GOGGLES Impact (I) / Dust & Splash (D&S) / Radiation (R)	WELDING HELMETS (W)	FACE SHIELDS (F)	HOODS (H)
FLYING OBJECTS						
Chipping, drilling	C	I	I	X	F	X
Grinding, buffing, polishing, etc.	C	D&S	D&S	X	F	X
Heavy sawing, planing	C	D&S	D&S	X	F	X
Wire & strip handling	C	—	—	X	X	X
Hammering, unpacking, nailing	C	—	—	X	F	X
FLYING PARTICLES, DUST, WIND						
Woodworking	C	D&S	D&S	X	F	X
Light metalworking & machining	C	D&S	D&S	X	F	X
Exposure to dust & wind	C	D&S	D&S	X	X	X
Painting	X	D&S	D&S	X	F	H
Concrete work, plastering	C	D&S	D&S	X	F	X
Material batching & mixing	C	D&S	D&S	X	F	X
HEAT, GLARE, SPARKS, MOLTEN SPLASH						
Spot welding, stud welding	X	See note 1 / R	See note 1 / R	X	See note 1 / F	X
ACID SPLASH, CHEMICAL BURNS						
Handling corrosive liquid	X	D&S	D&S	X	F	H

Operation						
Degreasing & pickling operations	X	D&S	D&S	X	F	X
Glass breakage	X	–	–	X	F	X
Chemical spraying	X	D&S	D&S	X	F	H
Liquid bitumen handling	X	D&S	D&S	X	F	X
ABRASIVE BLASTING						
Sand blasting	X	D&S	D&S	X	X	H
Shot blasting	X	X	X	X	X	H
Shot creting	X	X	X	X	X	H
GLARE, STRAY LIGHT (where slight reduction of visible light is required)						
Reflection, bright sun & lights	R	R	R	X	X	X
Reflected welding flash	R	R	R	X	X	X
Metal pouring	R	R	R	X	F*	X
Spot welding, stud welding	X	R	R	X	F	X
RADIATION (where moderate reduction of visible light is required)						
Gas cutting and welding	X	R	R	X	X	X
RADIATION (where large reduction of visible light is required)	See note 2			See note 2		
Electric arc welding	X	X	X	W	X	X
Heavy gas cutting	X	X	X	W	X	X
Plasma spraying & cutting	X	X	X	W	X	X
Inert gas shielded arc welding	X	X	X	W	X	X
Atomic hydrogen welding	X	X	X	W	X	X

X Not suitable

* Where injurious radiation is present, face shields must either comply with requirements for filters or must be used in conjunction with protectors having filters.

Note 1: For welding smaller studs, either eyecup goggles or cover goggles for radiation should be worn. A face shield should also be worn. For welding larger studs, a welding helmet should be worn.

Note 2: The practice of wearing safety spectacles with anti-flash lenses (shade 2.0 – 2.5) under welding helmets is strongly recommended to ensure impact and flash protection to the wearer when the helmet is raised or the hand shield is not in use. This is also recommended for anyone working near a welding operation.

- It is recommended that workers wear electric shock resistant footwear identified by a white rectangular label bearing the CSA trademark and the Greek letter omega in orange (Figure 18). This footwear does not provide absolute protection from electrocution but does provide some shock resistance in dry locations.

Skin Protection

Always dress suitably for work. Clothes are your first line of defence against hazards on the job. Items such as denim coveralls and long-sleeve cotton shirts protect you against minor scrapes and bruises as well as harmful ultraviolet exposure outdoors (Figure 19).

Regulations require protection where there is a risk of injury from contact between a workers's skin and
- a noxious gas, liquid, fume, or dust
- an object that may puncture, cut, or abrade the skin
- a hot object, hot liquid, or molten metal
- radiant heat.

Gloves are very effective against most minor cuts, scrapes, and abrasions. Gloves are recommended for work with sharp or abrasive materials.

Eye Protection

For basic eye protection, wear properly fitted industrial quality glasses with side shields. Table 1 classifies the most common construction activities under eight main hazard groups and outlines the types of eye protectors for each hazard group.

Specific classes of eye protectors should be matched to specific hazards.

Detailed consideration should be given to the severity of all hazards in selecting the most appropriate protector or combination of protectors.

The practice of requiring all personnel to wear spectacles with side shields is strongly recommended.

Optimum eye protection sometimes requires a combination of different classes of eye protectors.

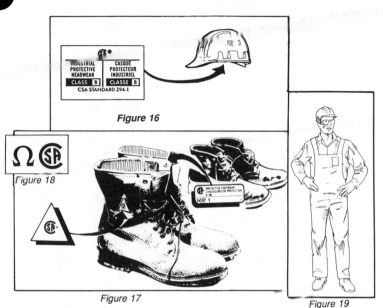

Figure 16

Figure 18

Figure 17

Figure 19

Hearing Protection

Each worker should have hearing protection available at work since continuous exposure to excessive noise from certain construction activities can lead to hearing loss.

Hearing protection is available in three general types (Figure 20):

- disposable ear plugs (made of pliable material, one size fits all but can be used only once)
- permanent plugs (must be fitted to provide a good seal but can be washed and reused)
- earmuffs (when properly fitted and worn, these generally provide more protection than earplugs).

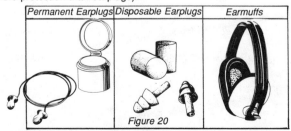

Permanent Earplugs	Disposable Earplugs	Earmuffs

Figure 20

Personnel working in noisy areas or with noisy equipment such as circular saws, hammer drills, and screw guns should wear hearing protection. Prolonged exposure to noise levels exceeding 90 decibels is harmful.

Table 2 illustrates maximum exposures for workers not equipped with hearing protection. For example, a worker exposed to 99 decibels is at risk after one hour, but could safely work the shift if properly fitted hearing protection is worn.

Unprotected Exposure Guide

Noise level (dBA)	Duration (Hours)
90	8
93	4
96	2
99	1
102	1/2
105	1/4
108 and up	No unprotected exposure

Table 2

*The decibel scale is **logarithmic.** For example, 93 decibels is **twice** as much noise as 90 decibels; 100 decibels is **ten times** more than 90.*

Fall-Arrest Systems

Regulations require that, unless a safety net or travel-restraint system is being used, a fall-arrest system must be worn if a worker may fall
– more than 3 metres
– into operating machinery
– into water or other liquids
– into or onto hazardous substances or objects.

A fall-arrest system consists of
– full body harness or safety belt (recommended for travel-restraint only)
– lanyard
– rope grab (or triple sliding hitch)
– lifeline
– lifeline anchor.

Figure 21 illustrates fall arrest components.

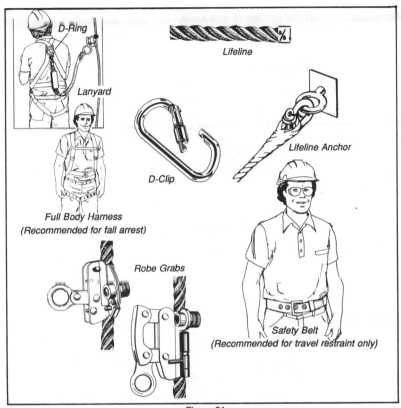

Figure 21
Safety Belts, Safety Harnesses, and Lanyards

All safety belts, full body harnesses, and lanyards should be CSA-certified (belts, harnesses, and lanyards will carry a CSA label).

Full body harnesses should be snug-fitting and worn with all hardware and straps intact and properly fastened.

Lanyards must be 16 millimetre (5/8") diameter nylon or equivalent.

When a lanyard is wire rope or nylon webbing, a shock absorber must be used.

Lanyards should be attached to the D-ring on the harness by a locking snap hook, a spliced loop and thimble, or a D-clip attached to a spliced loop and thimble.

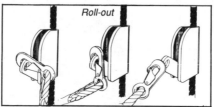

Figure 22

These precautions will prevent "roll-out" (Figure 22). This happens when a regular snap hook under load releases itself and rolls out from a connecting device, such as the small ring on older rope grabs.

Lifelines

All lifelines must be

− 16 millimetre diameter polypropylene or equivalent
− used by only one worker at a time
− free from any danger of chafing
− free of cuts, abrasions, and other defects
− long enough to reach the ground or knotted at the end to prevent the lanyard from running off the lifeline
− secured to a solid object (remember, the arrest load can be as high as 2,000 pounds).

Rope-Grabbing Devices

To attach the lanyard of a safety belt or safety harness to a lifeline, use a mechanical rope grab that meets CSA Standard Z259.2.

If a mechanical rope grab is not available, then use a triple sliding hitch (Figure 23). Keep the hitch tight on the lifeline at all times and ensure that it is kept high on the lifeline to reduce the fall distance.

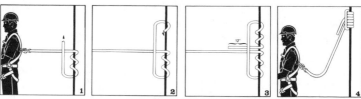

Figure 23

• Tie the hitch as illustrated. (The hitch may also be used with a lanyard on a safety harness.)
• Be sure to allow at least a 12-inch dead end.

- Tighten the hitch on the lifeline so the hitch won't slip.
- Position the hitch on the lifeline above head height.
- Lifeline must
  - reach the ground or
  - reach a secure and accessible level above the ground or
  - be knotted, cable-clipped, or otherwise provided with a positive stop to keep the hitch from running off the end of the lifeline.
- If you fall, do not grab the hitch, lanyard, or lifeline. To work properly, the hitch must come under a load.

Respiratory Protection

Construction personnel are sometimes exposed to respiratory hazards generated by equipment, materials, or procedures such as spray-painting and welding. Although proper work practices and engineered controls may be used to reduce these hazards, often the only practical control is respiratory protective equipment. Protection is ensured not only by the respirator but also by its proper selection and use.

To select the proper respirator for a particular job, you must know the characteristics of the hazard, the anticipated exposure, and the limitations of the equipment. Respiratory equipment should only be selected by someone who understands all three factors. Most manufacturers can assist with selection.

Respiratory hazards may be present as
- gases
- vapours
- fumes
- mists
- dusts.

Gases — Common toxic gases in construction are carbon monoxide from engine exhaust and hydrogen sulphide in sewers.

Vapours — Vapours are produced by solvents such as xylene, toluene, and mineral spirits used in paints, coatings, and degreasers.

Fumes — Welding fume is the most common type of fume in construction. Other examples include pitch fume from coal tar in built-up roofing and fume from diesel engines.

Mists — The spraying of paint, form oils, and other materials generates mists of varying composition.

Dusts — Dusts are generated by crushing, grinding, sanding, or cutting. Two common dusts in construction are fibrous dust from insulation materials and non-fibrous silica dust from sandblasting.

Controls

Work areas must be ventilated to reduce hazards from dusts, fumes, mists, gases or vapours.

Where ventilation is not practical, workers must be provided with respirators appropriate to the hazard and be trained to use and maintain the respirators properly.

Where disputes arise over the need for ventilation or the type of protection to be worn in a work area, the Ministry of Labour must be summoned to settle the dispute and advise the proper method and equipment to be used. Workers affected must not enter the area in question until the Ministry of Labour has resolved the dispute.

Respirators are divided into two types:
— air-purifying respirators purify inhaled air from the surrounding air but cannot replenish or increase its oxygen content
— supplied-air respirators deliver clean breathing air from a compressor or cylinder.

Use Table 3 as a general guide for matching respirator to hazard.

WARNING: Air-purifying respirators simply remove certain airborne hazards. They do **NOT** increase or replenish the oxygen content of the air and should never be worn in atmospheres containing less than 19.5% oxygen.

Air-Purifying Respirators

These devices purify the air drawn through them. Although various filters have been designed for specific hazards, there are two basic types used with air-purifying respirators: mechanical and chemical (Figure 24).

Mechanical filters remove solid particles such as dust and fume but provide no protection against hazardous gases or vapours. Chemical cartridge filters use substances which absorb or neutralize gases and vapours. Chemical cartridge filters include the following.

- Organic vapour cartridges remove vapours such as toluene, xylene, and mineral spirits found in paints, adhesives, and cleaners.
- Acid gas cartridges protect against limited concentrations of hydrogen chloride, sulphur dioxide, and chlorine.
- Ammonia cartridges designed especially to remove only ammonia gases.
- Combination cartridges can be used where more than one type of hazard exists.

Respirator cartridges and filters are colour-coded.

Dusts, Mists, Fume	Grey
Dust, Mist, Fume and Radionuclides	Purple/Magenta
Organic Vapour	Black
Acid Gases	White
Ammonia	Green
Acid Gases and Organic Vapours	Yellow

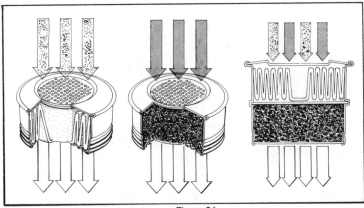

Figure 24

Table 3: Respirator Selection Guide

This table is intended as a guide only and is not applicable to every case. For activities not listed, additional information regarding the type of work, nature of material and working conditions is required and expert advice should be obtained.

Activity/Type of Exposure	Single-Use Dust Mask		Disposable Gas/Vapour Mask			Half-Face Mask			Full-Face Mask		PAPRs	Supplied-Air	
	Dust or Dust/Mist	Fume or High Efficiency Dust	Organic Vapour	Dust/Mist	High Efficiency Dust or Fume	Organic Vapour	Organic Vapour+ Dust/Mist	Acid Gas + Dust/Mist	Organic Vapour	Acid Gas	High Efficiency Dust or Fume	Hood or Helmet	SCBA or SCBA + Airline
Dust Exposures [1]													
Concrete cutting and breaking	●	●		●	●								
Refractory lining (except asbestos)	●	●		●	●						●		
Wood dust	●	●		●	●						●		
Pressure-treated wood dust	●	●		●	●								
Rock and gravel crushing	●	●		●	●								
Sandblasting (nozzle operator)												●	
Sandblasting (pot tender)	●	●		●	●								
Installation or removal of cellulose, fibreglass, mineral wool or calcium silicate insulation	●	●		●	●								
UFFI removal (well ventilated area)	●	●		●	●								
UFFI removal (poorly ventilated area)				●	●						●		
UFFI removal (wash-down stage using sodium bisulphite)								●		●			
Wet removal of chrysotile asbestos (usually fireproofing)					●								
Wet removal of amosite or crocidolite asbestos (usually pipe and boiler insulation)											●		
Dry removal of asbestos (all types)													●
Asbestos encapsulation?							●						
Removal of built-up roofing	●				●						●		

50

Painting

Spraying latex (water soluble paints)

Brush and roller application of alkyds and enamels (well ventilated areas)

Spraying alkyds and enamels (excluding epoxies and polyurethanes)

Spraying epoxy or polyurethane coatings

Application of any solvent-based alkyd, enamel, epoxy or polyurethane coating in confined areas

Welding and flame cutting [3]

Mild steel

Galvanized or plated metals

Stainless steel

Aluminum (by TIG or MIG process)[4]

Painted metals (in fairly well ventilated areas)

Painted or coated metals in confined areas

Demolition of painted steel structures

Miscellaneous

Heat welding single-ply roof membrane

Solvent or adhesive welding of single-ply roofing

Epoxy flooring application

PCB's (if heated to +55°C [130°F])[5]

Roofing kettlemen

---

[1] Where possible, water should be used to reduce dust concentration.

[2] Organic vapour cartridge is required to remove solvent vapours associated with many coating materials used for encapsulation.

[3] Preferred method of control is through fume collectors/exhausters.

[4] MIG or TIG welding of aluminum generates excessive amounts of ozone which can not be removed by typical air-purifying respirators.

[5] If the temperature of PCB's is kept below 55°C, there is little chance of generating much PCB vapour.

Supplied-Air Respirators

Although supplied-air respirators provide the best protection against many hazards, they present their own set of problems. With self-contained breathing apparatus (SCBA), there are problems with weight and limited service life. With airline units, the trailing hose can get snagged or tangled. Another concern relates to the quality of air stored in cylinders and supplied by compressors. For breathing, this air must meet high standards.

Facepieces

Five different styles of facepieces are available (Figure 25).

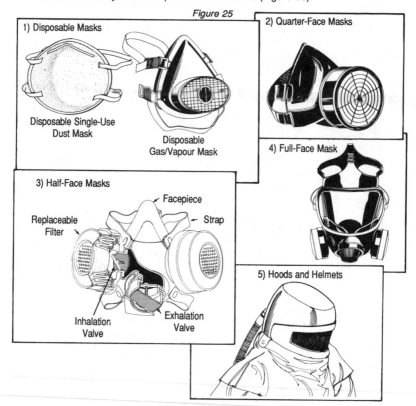

Figure 25

1) Disposable Masks

Disposable Single-Use Dust Mask

Disposable Gas/Vapour Mask

2) Quarter-Face Masks

3) Half-Face Masks

Facepiece

Replaceable Filter

Strap

Inhalation Valve

Exhalation Valve

4) Full-Face Mask

5) Hoods and Helmets

Fit Testing

With every respirator except hoods or helmets, a tight seal is required between facepiece and face. Positive or negative pressure tests can be used to check fit.

Negative Pressure Test — Block inlets. Inhale gently. Respirator should collapse slightly and not allow any air into facepiece (Figure 26).

Positive Pressure Test — Cover exhaust port and try to exhale gently. The facepiece should puff away from the face but no leakage should occur (Figure 27).

Cover inlets
and try
to inhale.

Figure 26
NEGATIVE PRESSURE FIT TEST

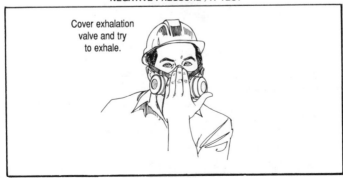

Cover exhalation
valve and try
to exhale.

Figure 27
POSITIVE PRESSURE FIT TEST

7 LADDERS

Every year in Ontario construction more than 800 lost-time injuries are caused by ladder accidents. Many of these accidents involve falls resulting in serious injuries and fatalities.

The following are major causes of accidents.

- Ladders are not held, tied off or otherwise secured.
- Slippery surfaces and unfavourable weather conditions cause workers to lose footing on rungs or steps.
- Workers fail to grip ladders adequately when climbing up or down.
- Workers take unsafe positions on ladders (such as leaning out too far).
- Placement on poor footing or at improper angles causes ladders to slide.
- Ladders are defective.
- High winds cause ladders to topple.
- Near electrical lines, ladders are carelessly handled or improperly positioned.

Wooden Ladders

- Never paint a wooden ladder. Paint hides signs of deterioration and may accelerate rotting by trapping moisture in the wood. Treat with a clear, non-toxic wood preservative or coat with a clear varnish.
- Inspect frequently for splits, shakes, or cracks in side rails and rungs, warping or loosening of rungs, loosening of metal hardware, and deformation of metal parts.

Aluminum Ladders

- Treat aluminum ladders with care. They are more liable to damage than wooden ladders.
- Because they conduct electricity well, never use aluminum ladders where electrical contact is possible.
- Check side rails and rungs regularly for dents, bends, and loose rungs. If repair by a competent person is not possible, the ladder should be destroyed.

Fiberglass Ladders

Fiberglass-reinforced plastic side rails do not conduct electricity well and are resistant to corrosion but heat-sensitive. They must not be exposed to temperatures above 93.2C (200F).

Inspect regularly for cracks and "blooming" — tufts of exposed glass fiber where the mat has worn off. Coat the worn area with an epoxy material compatible with the fiberglass.

Step, Trestle, and Platform Ladders

Step, trestle, and platform ladders (Figure 28) must have strong spreader arms which lock securely in the open position. Never stand on the top or pail shelf of a step ladder.

Fixed Ladders

Ladders permanently fixed to structures such as tanks, stacks, silos, and bins are often used by work crews during construction and renovation. Safety belts and lifelines or safety belts and channel lock devices must be used by workers ascending, descending, or working from the ladders. Safety belt devices are recommended even where safety cages are installed because the devices provide more positive fall protection than cages.

Job-built Ladders

Wood used for job-built ladders (Figure 29) should be straight-grained and free of loose knots, sharp edges, splinters, and shakes. The ladder should not be longer than 9 metres (30 feet). Used by many workers, job-built ladders deteriorate rapidly. They should be inspected every day or so. If defective, repair immediately or take out of service and destroy.

Use

- Check ladder for defects before use.
- Clear scrap and material away from the base and top of the ladder since getting on or off the ladder is relatively hazardous.
- Secure the base and top of the ladder against accidental movement. (Figure 30).

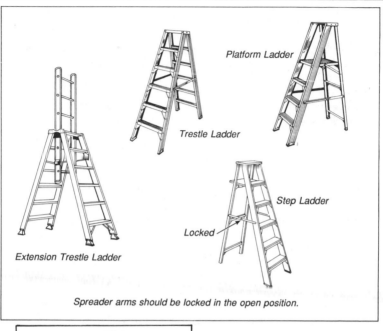

Platform Ladder

Trestle Ladder

Step Ladder

Locked

Extension Trestle Ladder

Spreader arms should be locked in the open position.

Figure 28

56

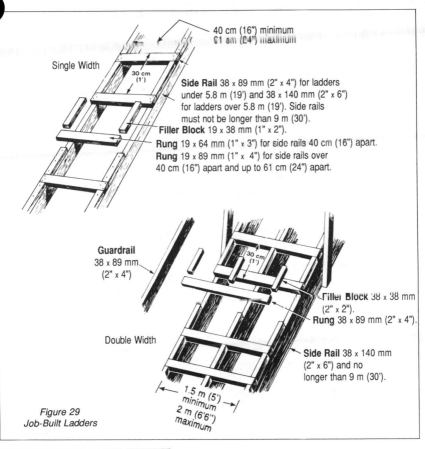

40 cm (16") minimum
61 cm (24") maximum

Single Width

30 cm (1')

Side Rail 38 x 89 mm (2" x 4") for ladders under 5.8 m (19') and 38 x 140 mm (2" x 6") for ladders over 5.8 m (19'). Side rails must not be longer than 9 m (30').

Filler Block 19 x 38 mm (1" x 2").

Rung 19 x 64 mm (1" x 3") for side rails 40 cm (16") apart.
Rung 19 x 89 mm (1" x 4") for side rails over 40 cm (16") apart and up to 61 cm (24") apart.

Guardrail 38 x 89 mm (2" x 4")

30 cm (1')

Filler Block 38 x 38 mm (2" x 2").
Rung 38 x 89 mm (2" x 4").

Double Width

Side Rail 38 x 140 mm (2" x 6") and no longer than 9 m (30').

1.5 m (5') minimum
2 m (6'6") maximum

Figure 29
Job-Built Ladders

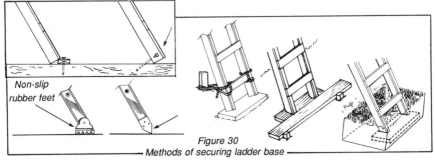

Non-slip rubber feet

Figure 30
Methods of securing ladder base

57

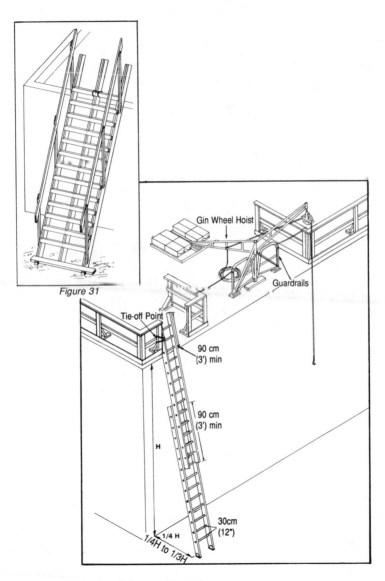

Figure 31

Gin Wheel Hoist

Guardrails

Tie-off Point

90 cm
(3') min

90 cm
(3') min

H

30cm
(12")

1/4 H

1/4H to 1/3H

Figure 32
Ladder Requirements

58

- Set the ladder on a firm, level surface. On soft, uncompacted, or rough soil, use a mud sill (Figure 30).
- Single-width job-built ladders are only meant for one worker at a time. A double-width ladder can be used by two workers providing they are on opposite sides (Figure 31).
- Make sure that rails on ladders extend at least 3 feet (90 cm) above the landing. This allows for secure grip while stepping on or off.
- Set straight or extension ladders one foot out for every 3 or 4 feet up, depending on length of ladder. See Figure 32 for ladder requirements.
- Before setting up ladders, always check for overhead powerlines.
- Do not position ladders against flexible or moveable surfaces.
- Always face the ladder when climbing up or down and while working from it.
- Maintain 3-point contact when climbing up or down. That means two hands and one foot or two feet and one hand on the ladder at all times.
- Keep your centre of gravity between the side rails. Your belt buckle should never be outside the side rails.
- When climbing up or down, do not carry tools or material in your hands. Use a hoist rope instead.
- Keep boots clean of mud, grease, or any slippery materials which could cause loss of footing.
- When working 3 metres (10 ft.) or more above the ground or floor, wear a safety belt or safety harness with the lanyard tied off to the structure.
- Never erect ladders on boxes, carts, tables, or other unstable surfaces.
- Use fall-arrest equipment such as ladder climbing devices or lifelines when working from long ladders or when climbing vertical fixed ladders.
- Vertical access ladders must

  - be fixed in position with side rails extending 900 mm (3 ft.) above the top landing
  - have rungs at least 150 mm (6 in.) away from the surface to which the ladder is attached
  - be offset at rest platforms at least every 9 metres (30 ft.), unless workers on the ladder use fall-arrest equipment
  - be equipped with a safety cage where workers may fall more than 3 metres (10 ft.).

- Never use ladders horizontally as scaffold planks, runways, or any other service they have not been designed for.
- Stand no higher than the third or fourth rung from the top. Maintain knee contact for balance.
- Do not splice short ladders together to make a long ladder. The side rails will not be strong enough for the extra loads.
- Do not use ladders for bracing. They are not designed for this type of loading.
- Do not set up ladders in doorways, passageways, driveways, or any other location where they can be struck or knocked over.
- Never rest a ladder on its rungs. Ladders must rest on their side rails.
- To erect long, awkward, or heavy ladders, get help to avoid injury from overexertion.
- Before erecting, using, or working from ladders, always check for electrical hazards. Never use aluminum ladders near live electrical equipment or wires.

Inspection and Maintenance

Ladders should only be repaired by personnel competent in this kind of work.

Defective ladders should be taken out of service and either tagged for repair or scrapped.

- Inspect ladders for structural rigidity.
- Inspect non-skid feet for wear, imbedded material, and proper pivot action on swivel feet.
- Replace frayed or worn ropes on extension ladders with type and size equal to manufacturer's original rope.
- Check aluminum ladder for dents and bends in side rails, steps, and rungs. Do not use metal pipe to replace a rung.
- Check wooden ladders for cracks, splits, and rot.
- Check all ladders for grease, oil, caulking, imbedded stone and metal, or other materials that could make them unsafe.

Trade Considerations

The carpentry, drywall, acoustic, and interior system trades rely heavily on ladders. Ministry of Labour statistics show that about 50% of all ladder accidents are related to work done from the ladder. About 30 to 40% of all ladder accidents involve unexplained loss of footing.

Trades working outdoors must always be aware of weather conditions and allow for additional margins of safety.

A surprising number of accidents occur when workers take the first step onto the bottom rung of a ladder. These falls are usually not serious but may cause sprains, fractures, and contusions that often result in lost-time injuries. The first step is often the point where the unstable, unsecured ladder will slide or tip.

Warning: Many ladder accidents occur when personnel are getting on or off the ladder.

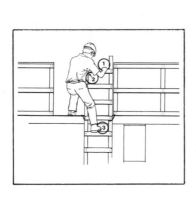 

Place both hands firmly on rungs before stepping onto a ladder.
Use 3-point contact when climbing up or down a ladder. That means two hands and one foot or two feet and one hand on the ladder at all times.
Clean mud and snow off your boots before climbing a ladder.

8 GUARDRAILS

A worker at risk of falling more than 3 metres must be protected by a safety net, a fall-arrest system, a travel-restraint system, or guardrails. In most cases, guardrails are the most common and convenient means of fall protection.

Areas to be protected include
- open edges of floors, mezzanines, and balconies
- open edges of scaffolds, platforms, and ramps
- openings in floors, roofs, and other working surfaces not otherwise covered or protected
- edges of slab formwork
- edges of bridge surfaces
- locations where a worker may fall into water, operating machinery, or hazardous substances.

Requirements

Basic requirements for wood guardrails are illustrated in Figure 33. Wood guardrails should have a top rail, mid-rail, and toeboard secured to vertical posts or supports with
- top rail between 91 cm (3 feet) and 1.07 metres (3 feet 6 inches) high
- toeboard at least 10.2 cm (4 inches) high and installed flush with the surface
- posts no more than 2.4 metres (8 feet) apart.

Wood-slat guardrails, wire rope, and manufactured wire mesh systems are also acceptable (Figure 34). They must, however, be at least as strong and durable as wooden guardrails, with the same minimum dimensions:

Guardrails must be capable of resisting any load likely to be applied. This means extra reinforcement in special situations, such as where forklifts or buggies are used.

Guardrails should be installed as close to the edge as possible.

Guardrails should be installed on balconies. It is not enough, for example, simply to barricade the entrance to a balcony.

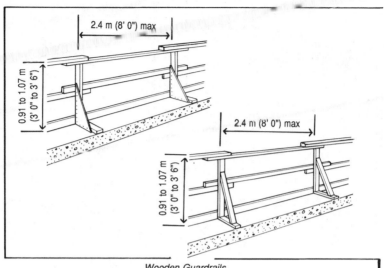

Wooden Guardrails

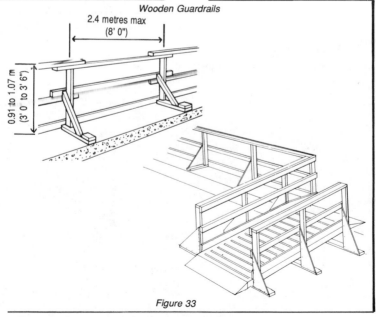

Figure 33

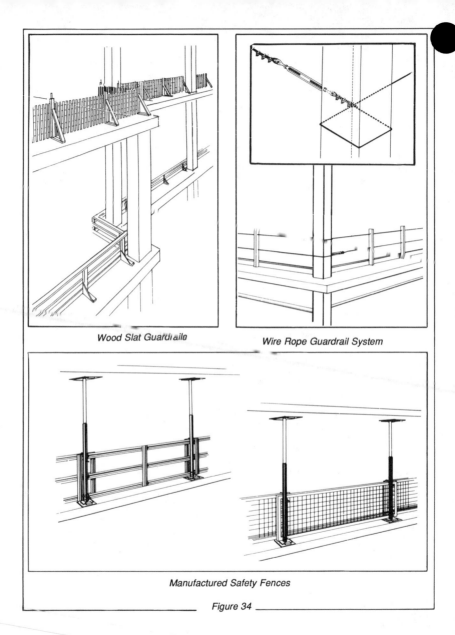

Wood Slat Guardrails

Wire Rope Guardrail System

Manufactured Safety Fences

Figure 34

64

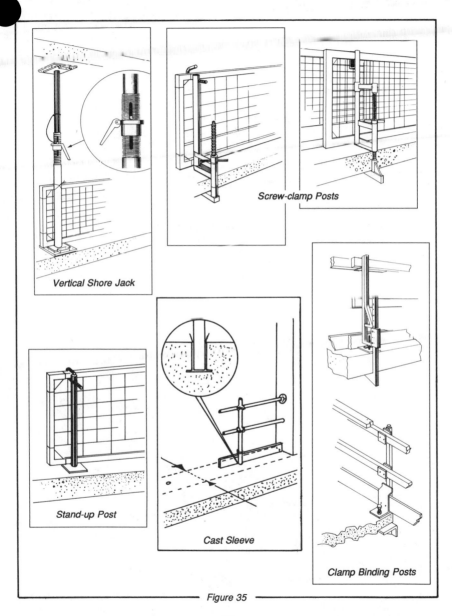

Vertical Shore Jack

Screw-clamp Posts

Stand-up Post

Cast Sleeve

Clamp Binding Posts

Figure 35

65

Supports

Typical methods of supporting wood guardrails are shown in Figure 33. Posts extending to top rail height must be braced and solidly fastened to the floor or slab.

Shoring jacks used as posts should be fitted with plywood softener plates top and bottom. Snug up and check the posts regularly for tightness.

For slabs and the end of flying slab forms, manufactured posts can be attached to the concrete with either clamps or inset anchors (Figure 35).

Maximum Strength

For maximum resistance to sideways force, the top rail of wooden guardrails should be laid flat, with the larger dimension horizontal.

To strengthen guardrails, reduce the spacing of posts to between 1 and 2 metres (3 feet 4 inches and 6 feet 8 inches) and double the 2 x 4 top rail. Posts on wooden guardrails must not be further apart than 2.4 metres (8 feet).

Where guardrails must be removed, the open edge should be roped off and marked with warning signs. In addition, workers inside the area should wear fall protection and make sure they are tied off (Figure 36).

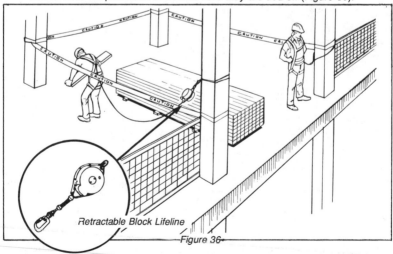

Retractable Block Lifeline
Figure 36

Floor Openings

Guardrails are the preferred method for protecting workers near floor openings but may not always be practical. Narrow access routes, for example, may rule them out. In such cases, securely fastened covers — planks, plywood, or steel plates — may be the best alternative.

Use 48 mm x 248 mm (1 7/8" x 9 3/4") full-sized No. 1 spruce planks. In some cases, pallet-like designs can make covers stronger and less likely to be removed (Figure 37).

Make opening covers stand out with bright paint. Include a warning sign such as DANGER! OPENING — DO NOT REMOVE.

Fasten the cover securely to the floor to prevent workers from removing it and falling through the opening.

Table 4 indicates load limits for two different spans and grades of planks for opening covers.

Table 4

Uniformly Distributed Load per sq foot	Up to 5-foot Span	Up to 7-foot Span
150 pounds	No. 1 Grade	Not allowed — load exceeds plank capacity
100 pounds	No. 1 Grade	Select Structural Grade
75 pounds	No. 1 Grade	No. 1 Grade

Notes:

1. Planks are spruce-pine-fir species group (SPF).
2. Planks are at least 1 7/8″ thick and 9 3/4″ wide.
3. Allowable stresses conform with CSA Standard CAN3-086-1984 "Engineering Design in Wood."
4. No stress increases are included for load sharing or load duration.
5. Width of opening should be no greater than span.
6. Loads indicated are maximum for grade and loading conditions, with cover completely "decked in" with planks.

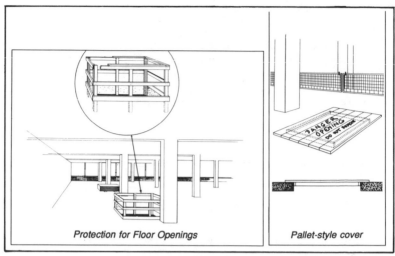

Protection for Floor Openings   Pallet-style cover

Figure 37

Stairs

The open edges of stairs require guardrail protection. Specifications for a wooden arrangement are shown in Figure 38.

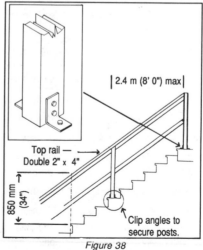

2.4 m (8' 0") max

Top rail —
Double 2" x 4"

850 mm
(34")

Clip angles to
secure posts.

Figure 38
Guardrails on Stairs

9 SCAFFOLDS

Problem Areas

> Over 600 scaffold accidents occur annually in Ontario
> construction. More than half of these are falls. Fatalities are also
> related to scaffolds each year.

- erecting and dismantling scaffolds
- climbing up and down scaffolds
- planks sliding off or breaking
- platforms not fully planked or "decked"
- platforms without guardrails
- failure to install all required components such as base plates,
  connections, and braces
- moving rolling scaffolds near overhead electrical wires
- moving rolling scaffolds with workers on the platform.

Selection

Choose the right system for the job (Figure 39). Considerations include

- the weight of workers, tools, materials, and equipment to be carried
  by the scaffold
- site conditions (interior, exterior, backfill, concrete floors, variations in
  elevation, and so on)
- height to which scaffold will be erected
- type of work to be done from the scaffold
- duration of work
- experience of supervisor and crew
- requirements for pedestrian traffic
- weather conditions
- ladders or other access
- obstructions
- building configuration
- special erection or dismantling problems.

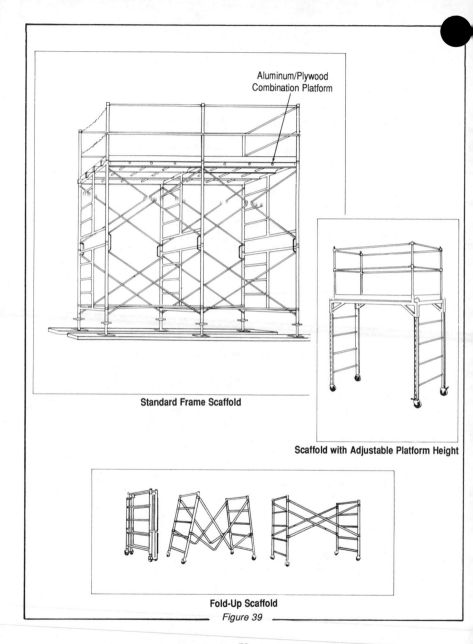

Aluminum/Plywood
Combination Platform

Standard Frame Scaffold

Scaffold with Adjustable Platform Height

Fold-Up Scaffold

Figure 39

70

Erecting and Dismantling Frame Scaffolds

The erection, alteration, and dismantling of scaffolds must be carried out under the supervision of a competent person.

Inspection

Before use, inspect scaffold materials for

- damage to frames, braces, and other structural components
- damage to hooks on manufactured platforms
- splits, knots, and dry rot in planks
- de-lamination of laminated veneer planks
- compatibility of components
- enough components for the job.

Structural components bent, damaged, or severely rusted should not be used. Defective planks should be removed from the site so they cannot be used for platform material

Before erecting a scaffold, check the location for
- ground conditions
- overhead wires
- obstructions
- variations in surface elevation
- tie-in locations and methods.

Support Surface

Scaffolds must be erected on surfaces which can support all loads to be applied.

Floors are usually adequate to support scaffold loads of workers, tools, and light materials. Older wooden floors should be examined to ensure that they will support the anticipated loads. Shoring below the floor and directly under the scaffold legs may be necessary. Or sills which span the floor support structure may be required.

To support scaffolds, backfilled soils must be well compacted and levelled. Mud and soft soil should be replaced with compacted gravel or crushed stone.

Where mudsills must be placed on sloping ground, the area should be levelled, wherever possible, by excavating rather than backfilling (Figure 40). It may be necessary to use half-frames to accommodate grade changes (Figure 41).

Mudsills should be 2" x 10" planks (full size) and continuous under at least two consecutive supports. Scaffold feet should rest centrally on the mudsill and the sill should, where possible, project at least 2 feet beyond the scaffold foot at ends or where individual sills butt together. Mudsills may be placed along the length or across the width of frames (Figure 42).

Blocking or packing with shims under scaffold feet or mudsills is bad practice (Figure 43).

Assembly

Install all parts, fittings, and accessories in accordance with manufacturers' instructions. Always use base plates. They allow for minor adjustments to keep the scaffold plumb and level. Nail base plates to mudsills.

- Bracing in the vertical plane is a must on both sides of every frame (Figure 44).
- Bracing in the horizontal plane should be provided at the joint of every third tier of frames.
- Horizontal bracing should coincide with the point at which the scaffold is tied to the building or structure being worked on.
- Horizontal bracing on the first tier helps to square up the scaffold before base plates are nailed to mudsills.

Every scaffold manufacturer provides coupling devices to join scaffold frames together (Figure 45). Install these devices properly on every leg of the scaffold at every joint as assembly proceeds.

Wheels or castors should be securely attached to the scaffold and equipped with brakes.

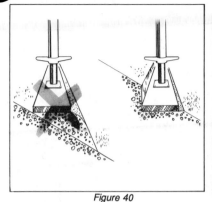

Figure 40

On sloping ground, excavate rather than backfill to provide level footing.

Figure 41

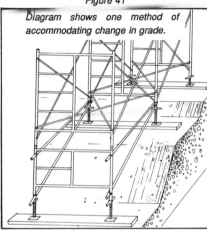

Diagram shows one method of accommodating change in grade.

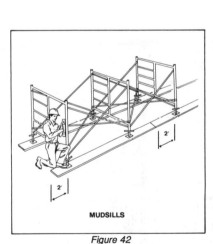

MUDSILLS

Figure 42

Mudsills should extend at least 2' beyond leg of scaffold at joints and ends.

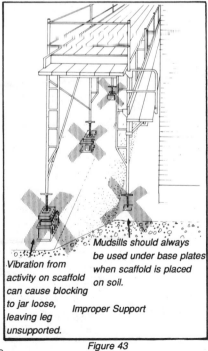

Mudsills should always be used under base plates when scaffold is placed on soil.

Vibration from activity on scaffold can cause blocking to jar loose, leaving leg unsupported.

Improper Support

Figure 43

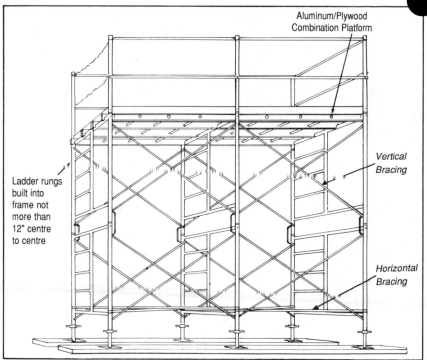

Aluminum/Plywood
Combination Platform

Vertical
Bracing

Ladder rungs
built into
frame not
more than
12" centre
to centre

Horizontal
Bracing

Figure 44

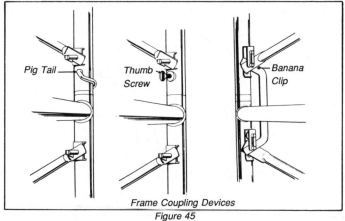

Pig Tail

Thumb
Screw

Banana
Clip

Frame Coupling Devices
Figure 45

74

Always install guardrails. When the scaffold reaches the desired level, put up a guardrail. This applies to all scaffolds regardless of height. If manufactured guardrails are not available, use 2" x 4" or tube-and-clamp guardrails (Figure 46)

Braces should slide into place easily. If force is required, either the braces are bent or damaged or the frames are out of plumb.

Braces should be secured at each end. Ensure that self-locking devices move freely and fall into place.

Where frames are not equipped with ladder rungs, install ladders as each tier goes up. Climbing up and down scaffolds frequently leads to injuries which ladders can help prevent.

When the first tier of scaffold is erected check for plumb. Settlement or slight variations in the fit of the components may require adjustments as tiers are added to the scaffold tower. The scaffold frame should be checked for plumb after each tier is added.

Frame scaffold components are shown in Figure 47.

Platforms

All parts and fittings should be secure before platform components are put in place.

To proceed with the next tier, workers should lift platform sections or planks from the previous tier leaving either one platform section or two planks. Workers then have platforms to stand on when erecting or dismantling the platform above.

Frequently, low scaffolds, one or two frames in height, are not fully decked in. This leads to accidents and injury.

A well wheel or "gin" wheel and hoist arm or davit makes hoisting materials easier (Figure 48).

The wheel and arm allow hoisting to be done by workers on the ground. This eliminates the risk or workers falling from the scaffold platform as they pull materials up by rope. Loads lifted by a well wheel should be no more than 100 lbs.

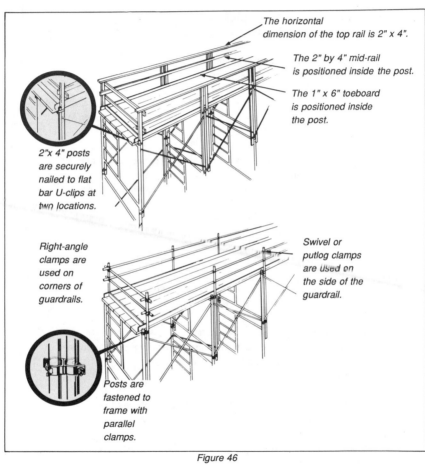

The horizontal dimension of the top rail is 2" x 4".

The 2" by 4" mid-rail is positioned inside the post.

The 1" x 6" toeboard is positioned inside the post.

2"x 4" posts are securely nailed to flat bar U-clips at two locations.

Right-angle clamps are used on corners of guardrails.

Swivel or putlog clamps are used on the side of the guardrail.

Posts are fastened to frame with parallel clamps.

Figure 46
Guardrails

Frame Scaffold Components

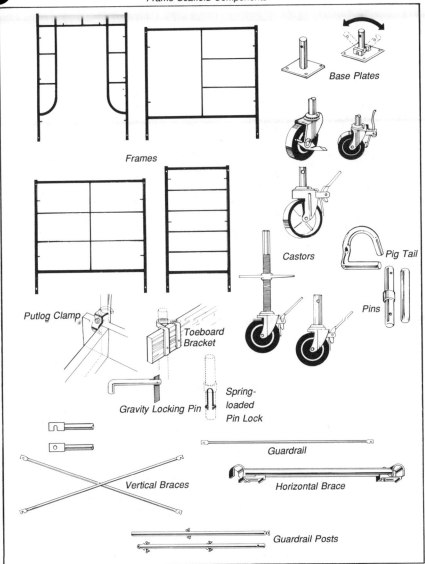

Base Plates

Frames

Castors

Pig Tail

Pins

Putlog Clamp

Toeboard Bracket

Spring-loaded Pin Lock

Gravity Locking Pin

Guardrail

Vertical Braces

Horizontal Brace

Guardrail Posts

Figure 47

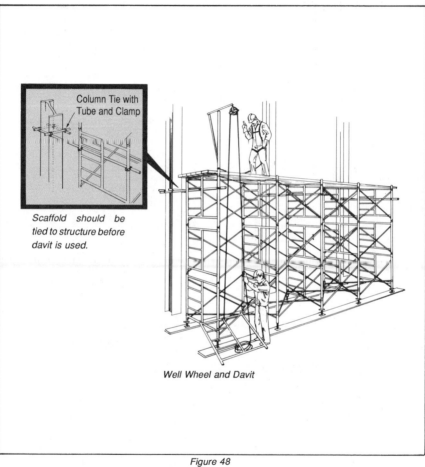

Column Tie with Tube and Clamp

Scaffold should be tied to structure before davit is used.

Well Wheel and Davit

Figure 48

Tie-ins

Always tie in the scaffold as erection proceeds (Figure 49).

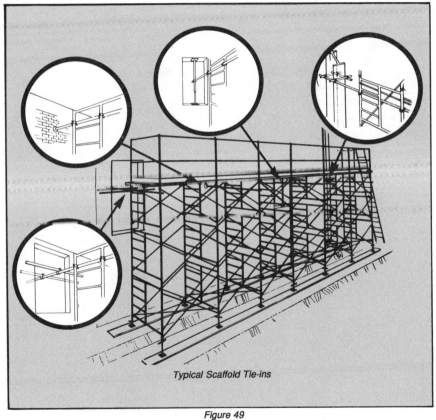

Typical Scaffold Tie-ins

Figure 49

Scaffold Stability

Three-to-One Rule — On a scaffold the ratio of height to least lateral dimension should not exceed 3 to 1 unless
- the scaffold is tied into the structure
- the scaffold is properly stabilized by guy wires or
- the scaffold is secured by outrigger stabilizers sufficient to maintain the ratio (Figure 50).

Outrigger stabilizers are available for both frame and tube-and-clamp systems.

Stabilizers widen the base of a scaffold and allow it to rise proportionally higher. But stabilizers must be equally extended on each side of the scaffold to meet the three-to-one rule (Figure 51).

Figure 50
Rolling Scaffold with Outrigger Stabilizers

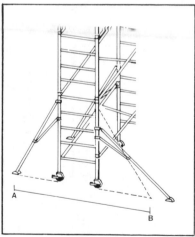

Figure 51
3-to-1 rule applies
only over distance AB.

Dismantling

Dismantling proceeds in reverse order to erection. Each tier should be completely dismantled and lowered to the ground before the next tier is dismantled.

When scaffolds have been up for a long time, pins and other components frequently rust, braces become bent, and materials such as paint build up on parts. All of these can prevent components from separating. Workers should wear a safety belt and lanyard tied off to a scaffold frame or lifeline before attempting to loosen stuck or jammed parts.

Erecting and Dismantling Tube-and-Clamp Scaffolding

Tube-and-clamp scaffolds should only be erected by a skilled, experienced crew. The typical erection sequence is shown in Figure 52. A typical set-up is illustrated in Figure 53.

Clamps

The following clamps are commonly used:
- **right angle clamp** for connecting tubes at right angles to provide rigidity.
- **end-to-end clamp** externally applied to connect two tubes end-to-end.
- **swivel clamp** to connect two tubes where right-angle clamps cannot be used. Often applied to connect bracing in the structure.
- **parallel clamp** for lap-jointing two tubes together and for connecting guardrail posts to the standards or legs of frame scaffolds.
- **concrete tie clamp** to connect a tube to concrete or other surfaces using a bolt or concrete anchor.
- **putlog clamp** to connect two tubes in light-duty service such as guardrails or to secure wooden items such as toeboards.

Before use, check clamps carefully for damage to threads and body.

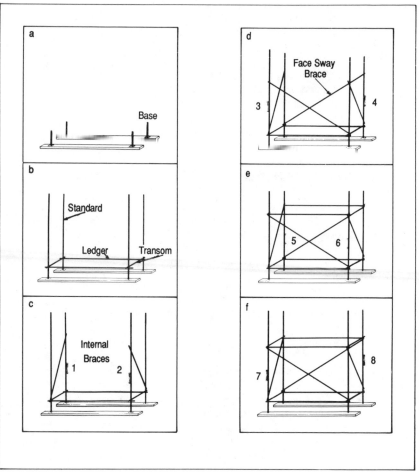

Figure 52
Erection Sequence:
Tube-and-Clamp Scaffold

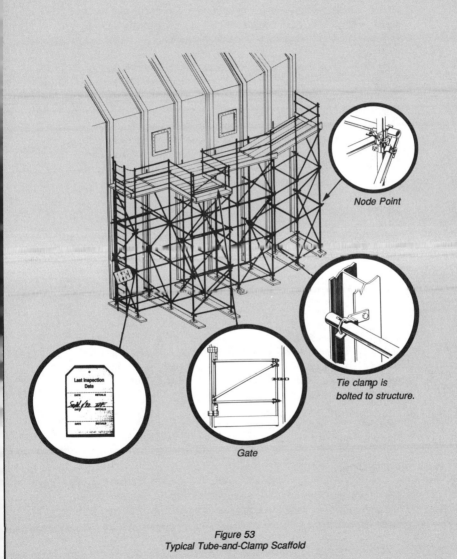

Node Point

Tie clamp is
bolted to structure.

Last Inspection
Date

Gate

Figure 53
Typical Tube-and-Clamp Scaffold

Assembly

Wherever possible, tube-and-clamp scaffolding makes use of a bay and elevation spacing of about 2 metres (6 ft. 6 in.) longitudinally and vertically. A complete system is shown in Figure 54.

Ledgers should be connected to standards using right-angle clamps. Transoms should be placed above the ledgers and both should be levelled and kept horizontal. Transoms may be connected to standards or ledgers by right-angle clamps.

Joints in standards and ledgers should be made with end-to-end clamps. These joints should be as close to the node points as possible. A node point is the point at which the ledger-to-standard, transom-to-standard, and bracing-to-standard connections come together (Figure 55).

Tie-ins

Tie-ins should be located at every second node vertically and every third standard horizontally. Connections should be made with right-angle clamps. Tie-ins should be capable of withstanding both tension (pull) and compression (push).

Bracing

Internal bracing is connected standard-to-standard using swivel clamps as close to the node as possible. Internal bracing should normally be placed at every third standard. Location should coincide with tie-in points. Bracing for tube-and-clamp scaffolding must always be installed as erection progresses.

Face sway bracing should be installed to the full height of the scaffold. It may be located in a single bay or extend across several bays.

Dismantling

Dismantling must proceed in reverse order to erection. Each tier should be completely dismantled as far as connections will allow before the lower tier is started.

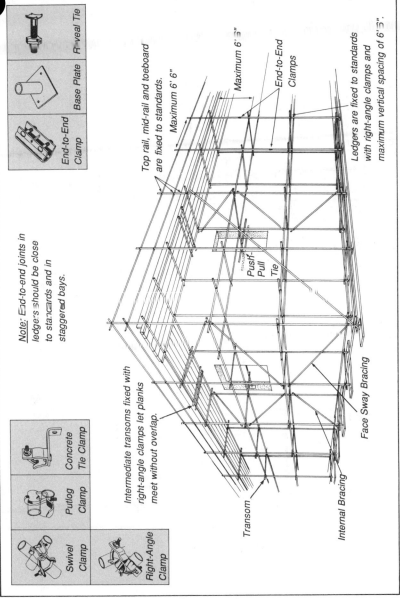

Figure 54

Reveal Tie | Base Plate | End-to-End Clamp

Concrete Tie Clamp | Putlog Clamp | Swivel Clamp | Right-Angle Clamp

Note: End-to-end joints in ledgers should be close to standards and in staggered bays.

Top rail, mid-rail and toeboard are fixed to standards.

Maximum 6' 6"

Maximum 6' 6"

End-to-End Clamps

Ledgers are fixed to standards with right-angle clamps and maximum vertical spacing of 6' 6".

Push-Pull Tie

Intermediate transoms fixed with right-angle clamps let planks meet without overlap.

Transom

Face Sway Bracing

Internal Bracing

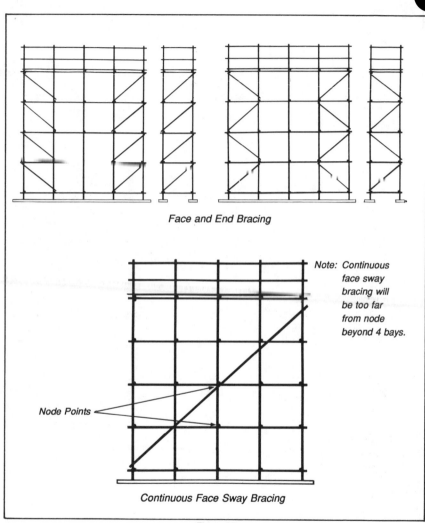

Face and End Bracing

Note: Continuous face sway bracing will be too far from node beyond 4 bays.

Node Points

Continuous Face Sway Bracing

Figure 55
Bracing

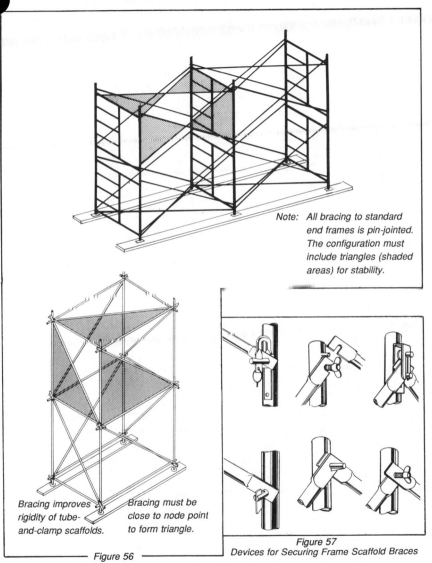

Note: All bracing to standard end frames is pin-jointed. The configuration must include triangles (shaded areas) for stability.

Bracing improves rigidity of tube-and-clamp scaffolds.

Bracing must be close to node point to form triangle.

Figure 56
Bracing Showing Triangles for Stability

Figure 57
Devices for Securing Frame Scaffold Braces

Stability

For any structure with pin joints, such as scaffolding, the basic bracing system must be made up of triangles (Figure 56). This applies to both frame and tube-and-clamp scaffolding.

Standard end frames are rigid and do not require triangular braces. However, they are connected by pin joints and require triangular bracing in both the horizontal and vertical planes.

Tube-and-clamp structures are not as rigidly fixed as frames. Bracing must therefore be provided in both vertical planes

Tall scaffold towers or rolling scaffolds must have horizontal bracing to keep the structure square and prevent the scaffold from folding up.

Braces with kinks, bends, or deformations should not be used.

Bracing must be adequately secured in place. Locking devices must operate freely for ease of erection and dismantling (Figure 57).

Platform Materials

The rated load-carrying capacity of platform panels should be obtained from the supplier and marked on the panel if not there already.

Laminated veneer lumber is used increasingly as platform material. Rated working loads should be identified. Inspect veneer lumber for peeling, blistering, and rot.

Planks must be at least 48 mm x 248 mm (1 7/8" x 9 3/4") and must meet or exceed the requirements for number 1 grade spruce-pine-fir (SPF). Select structural grades of SPF or Douglas fir are strongly recommended. Inspect planks regularly and discard if defective (Figure 58).

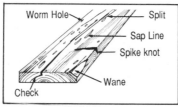

Figure 58

88

Platforms must be secured against sliding or movement. Platform panels have hooks which will slide sideways on the scaffold unless the platform is fully decked in (Figure 59).

Table 5: Maximum Loads on Planks For Scaffold Platforms 5' in Width

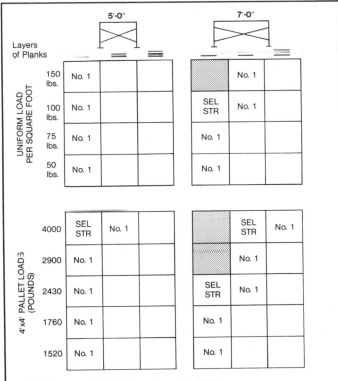

		5'-0"			7'-0"		
UNIFORM LOAD PER SQUARE FOOT	150 lbs.	No. 1			(shaded)	No. 1	
	100 lbs.	No. 1			SEL STR	No. 1	
	75 lbs.	No. 1			No. 1		
	50 lbs.	No. 1			No. 1		
4'x4' PALLET LOAD (POUNDS)	4000	SEL STR	No. 1		(shaded)	SEL STR	No. 1
	2900	No. 1			(shaded)	No. 1	
	2430	No. 1			SEL STR	No. 1	
	1760	No. 1			No. 1		
	1520	No. 1			No. 1		

1. Planks are **spruce-pine-fir species group (SPF).**
2. Planks are at least 1 7/8" thick and at least 9 3/4" wide.
3. Grade is either number one (No. 1) or select structural (SEL STR).
4. Allowable stresses conform with CSA Standard CAN3-086-1984 "Engineering Design in Wood."
5. No stress increases are included for load sharing or load duration.
6. Scaffold platforms are 5' wide and fully decked in.
7. Loads indicated are **maximum** for grade and loading conditions. Shaded areas indicate that **no** SPF grades are capable of carrying the loads.

Table 5

Planks should be cleated on at least one end to prevent movement (Figure 60). The platform should be fully decked in to prevent sideways movement. Maximum loads for planks are shown in Table 5.

Rolling scaffolds should have brakes on all wheels or castors. Brakes should be applied once the scaffold is in position. Secure wheels or castors to the frame so they won't drop off crossing a hole or depression

Rolling scaffolds should always
– have guardrails
– be securely pinned together
– have horizontal bracing.

Rolling scaffolds over one frame high should not be moved with anyone on the platform. If movement is necessary with workers aboard, they must wear full body harnesses tied off to a fixed, independent support. The travel area must be firm and level.

Scaffold Use

Ladder rails must project 1 metre (3 feet) above the scaffold platform. Keep areas around top and bottom of ladders clear.

Use 3-point contact to climb ladders. This means two hands and one foot or two feet and one hand on the ladder at all times. Always face the ladder and keep your centre of gravity between the rails.

There may be situations where scaffolds must be used without guardrails. Personnel on the platform must use a fall-arrest system.

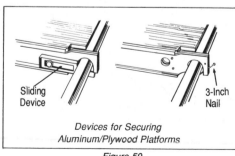

Sliding
Device

3-Inch
Nail

*Devices for Securing
Aluminum/Plywood Platforms*

Figure 59

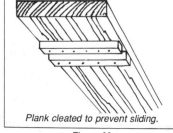

Plank cleated to prevent sliding.

Figure 60

10 POWERED ELEVATING WORK PLATFORMS

Regulations

The *Regulations for Construction Projects* include the following requirements.

- Elevating work platforms must be engineered and tested to meet National Standards of Canada.

- The devices must be checked each day before use.

- The owner must keep a log of all inspections, tests, repairs, modifications, and maintenance.

- The log must be kept up-to date and include names and signatures of persons who performed inspections and other work.

- A maintenance and inspection record tag must be attached near the operator's station and include the date of the last maintenance and inspection and the name and signature of the person performing the work.

- Workers must be given oral and written instructions before using the platform for the first time. Instruction must include items to be checked daily before use.

- Instruction must cover
  - manufacturer's requirements
  - load limitations
  - hands-on demonstration of all controls
  - limitations of surface for which platform is designed.

- An elevating work platform
  - must not be loaded in excess of its rated working load
  - must be used on a firm level surface
  - must be operated according to manufacturer's written instructions

- must not be loaded in ways that affect stability or endanger a worker
- must not be moved unless each worker aboard is protected by a safety belt attached to the platform.

- An operator's manual must be kept with the elevating work platform while it is on a project.

Problems

There have been relatively few accidents with elevating work platforms. When accidents do happen, however, they can involve serious injury and extensive damage. Injuries most frequently occur when workers are getting on and off the platform.

Accident causes include
- lack of operator training on the model being used
- using the wrong machine for the job
- lifting materials improperly
- poor maintenance.

Training – Poor or non-existent training is the major problem. Often personnel do not understand the basic limitations of the machines they are required to operate. The Construction Safety Association of Ontario offers a generic training program. This must be supplemented by specific instruction on basic items when the worker has not previously operated a similar model of machine.

Selection – Elevating work platforms are designed for different uses. It's essential to have the right machine for the job. Typical mistakes are
- using an on-slab device where a rough-terrain unit is required
- using an undersized unit for lifting materials
- lifting materials that stick out too far from the platform
- using a scissor lift where a boom-type would be more appropriate
- extending the platform with planks, ladders, or other devices because the machine does not reach the required height.

Selection factors include
- lifting capacity
- surface conditions

- platform size and configuration
  mobility
- material to be lifted
- access
- terrain or building obstructions
- degree of operator training and skill.

Lifting – One of the most important features with scissor lifts is the ability to lift materials and equipment to the work area. Problems with stability and balance occur, however, when material sticks out too far, is stacked off-centre, or is not secured.

Maintenance – Maintenance responsibilities shared by all are sometimes met by none. Equipment suppliers, construction contractors, and operators must ensure that inspection and maintenance meet manufacturer's requirements.

Figure 61 indicates location of the following maintenance and inspection points for a scissor lift.

1) Check platform/guardrails – Guardrails in place; control panel secured; access ladder in good condition.
2) Check tires for inflation when applicable.
3) Check level of hydraulic oil in reservoir.
4) Check lug nuts on wheels.
5) Check joints, pins, and bushings – lubrication; no loose or damaged bushings or pins.
6) Check tire rod linkage – no loose or missing parts; no visible damage; tie rod end studs locked.
7) Check batteries are fully charged – if electrically powered. If internal combustion engine, check oil/fuel.
8) Check ground control panel – switches operable; no visible damage; placards secure and legible.
9) Check hydraulic supply lines/cylinders – no leaks; no loose or unsecured hose; hose guards in place and undamaged.
10) Check platform control panel – all controls operable; undamaged; placards secure and legible.

Note: If equipped with outriggers or stabilizers, check cylinders for leakage or cracks.

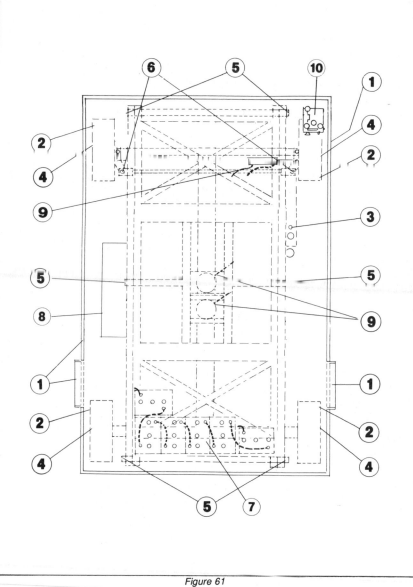

Figure 61

94

Figure 62 shows the location of the following maintenance and inspection points for a boom-type machine.

1) Check platform and guardrails – no loose or missing parts or visible damage. Lock pins in place.
2) Check hose and cable guards on boom – properly secured; no damage to guards, hoses, and cables.
3) Check drive motors and brake shields – securely bolted in place; no leaks or missing hardware.
4) Check drive hub – no visible damage or evidence of leakage.
5) Check tires and wheels – no cut tires; tires properly inflated; no missing lug nuts; no leaks; no rim damage.
6) Check frame – no bends or other damage; no loose or missing hardware.
7) Check fuel supply – adequate fuel, filler cap in place; no damage, leaks, or spills.
8) Check power track – no visible damage to hydraulic or electrical lines.
9) Check boom pivot shaft – must be properly secured and lubricated.
10) Check lift cylinder – rod end shaft properly secured.
11) Check tie rods and linkage – no visible damage, loose or missing parts; no steering cylinder leaks.
12) Check engine oil – full mark on dip stick with filler cap secured.
13) Check ground control panel – switches operable; placards legible; no visible damage.
14) Check counterweight – properly secured.
15) Check exhaust system – no leaks or damage.
16) Check engine air filter – oil in bowl clean and precleaner free of dirt.
17) Check battery – proper electrolyte level; cables tight with no corrosion.
18) Check hydraulic oil level – full on dipstick with all systems shut down and boom stowed.
19) Check hydraulic oil filter – indicator at proper position with engine operating at full throttle and oil warmed up.
20) Check turntable and pinion – evidence of lubrication; no loose or missing hardware or damage.
21) Check boom – no visible damage; wear pads secure.
22) Check platform pivots and cylinder – pins properly secured with evidence of lubrication; no cylinder leaks.

23) Check platform control console – switches and levers properly secured and free to return to neutral position; no loose or missing parts; no visible damage.

24) Check extending axles (if so equipped) – axle lock pins properly installed; no evidence of leakage; no loose or missing parts; no visible damage.

Note: Check placards. All placards and instructions should be secure and legible.

Tying-off – Workers must tie off to the platform when the device is being moved. This can be a travel-restraint system. Tying off to the lower guardrail should be adequate where the guardrail is secured to the platform and no other suitable tie-off point has been provided.

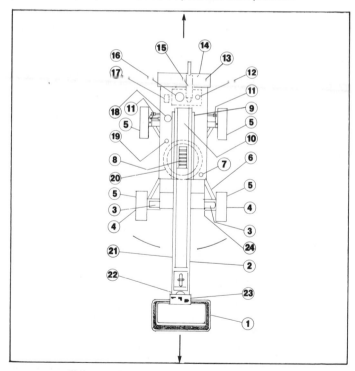

Figure 62

Types

Push-arounds - For smooth, level, hard, on-slab conditions. Must be pushed or independently powered. Many fold up to pass through standard doors. Safer and more economical than scaffolding in some cases. Limited by lack of mobility under their own power. Figure 63.

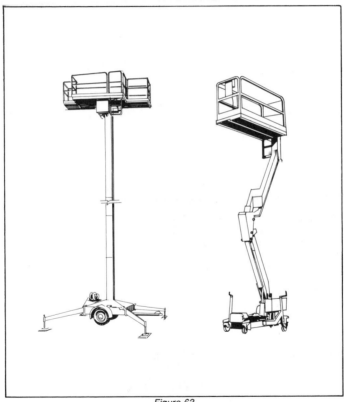

Figure 63
Push-Around Powered Platforms

Powered on-slab machines - Scissor lifts, though all may not be technically scissor-operated. Some have extendible one-person platforms; others have platforms that rotate. For use on smooth, level, hard surfaces free of holes and depressions. **Not** to be used in the raised position on slopes greater than 1-in-50. Minimum capacity recommended for construction: 700 lbs. Figure 64.

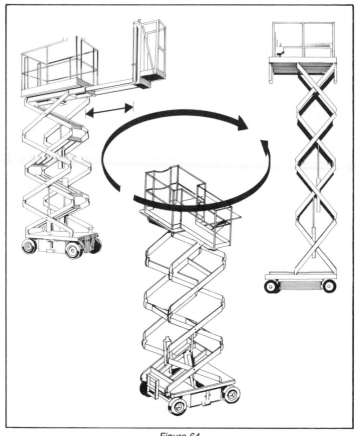

Figure 64
On-Slab Powered Platforms

Powered rough terrain machines. Similar in design to on-slab units but with undercarriages and power to handle off-slab conditions. Minimum capacity recommended for construction: 1000 lbs. On some units, outriggers must be deployed to achieve the rated lifting capacity. Rough terrain must be firm and relatively level. Figure 65.

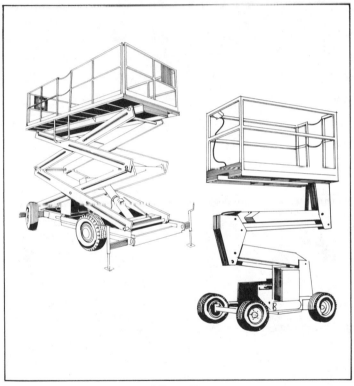

Figure 65
Off-Slab Powered Platforms

Powered boom platforms - Designed for on-slab or off-slab. Platform or bucket on extendible rotating boom. Some booms articulated for getting around obstructions. Platform capacity may change with boom length, boom angle, and surface conditions. Consult the load chart, though most boom-type platforms have only a single rated working load. Some with outriggers or extendible axles for stability at maximum boom reach. Centre of gravity can shift depending on boom extension and angle. Operators must be well trained and skilled. Figure 66.

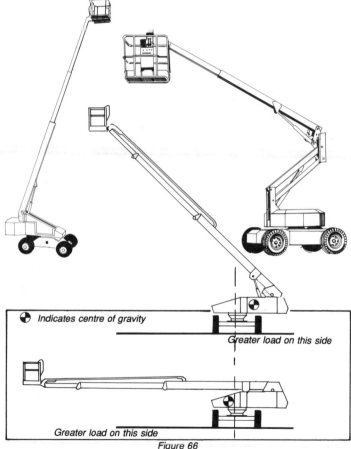

Indicates centre of gravity

Greater load on this side

Greater load on this side

Figure 66
How boom orientation affects centre of gravity and load on wheels

Operation

For the specific unit they will use, operators must know
- manufacturer's operating manual
- manufacturer's warning and caution signs on the machine
- location of all emergency controls
- daily maintenance checks to perform
- applicable regulations.

Training applies only to a particular make and model. If other units are to be operated, appropriate training must be provided.

The following are general guidelines for operation.

- Always check for overhead powerlines before moving the machine or operating the platform. Observe limits of approach around live electrical wires and equipment.

Voltage Rating of Powerline	Minimum Distance
750 to 150,000 volts	3 metres (10')
150,001 to 250,000 volts	4.5 metres (15')
over 250,000 volts	6 metres (20')

- Before leaving the machine unattended, lock or otherwise prevent its unauthorized use.

- Keep platform load below maximum rated working load (RWL) — preferably below 2/3 of RWL.

- Make sure that all controls are labelled with action and direction.

- Keep guardrails in good condition and make sure that chain or gate at opening is secure before moving platform.

- Shut off power and insert required props before servicing machine or checking for problems.

- Never remove guardrails when platform is raised.

- Don't jam controls through neutral to reverse direction of movement or operation. Move control gradually, pausing slightly in neutral, for safer, smoother operation.

- Deploy stabilizers or outriggers according to manufacturer's instructions.

- Position boom in line with direction of travel wherever possible.

- Keep ground personnel away from machine and out from under platform or bucket.

- Never allow workers to walk the boom to get on or off the platform or bucket.

- Never try to move, push, lift, or free the machine by telescoping the boom.

- Make sure that extension cords are long enough to reach the expected platform height.

11 SUSPENDED ACCESS EQUIPMENT

On average, two fatalities and over 100 lost-time injuries are connected with suspended access equipment each year in Ontario construction.

This equipment includes suspended platforms, suspended scaffolds, work cages, and bosun's chairs.

Training in the proper selection, rigging, operation, and maintenance of equipment is essential. The use of fall-arrest systems must be a major part of instruction.

Engineered Designs

Section 139 of the *Regulations for Construction Projects* requires designs by a professional engineer for any suspended scaffold
- that consists of more than one platform, or
- that, together with its components, weighs more than 525 kg (1,160 lbs.).

The design drawings must include
. size and material specifications for all components
. maximum live load on platform
  engineer's statement that design meets regulations
. engineer's signature and seal.

The system must be
. erected according to the design
. inspected by the engineer
. approved in writing by the engineer.

No one should use the suspended scaffold until these requirements have been met. The constructor must keep the design drawings and engineer's statement of approval on the project as long as the system is in place.

Workers who must use suspended scaffolds consisting of more than one platform or weighing more than 525 kg (1,160 lbs.) should review the design drawings with management.

Fall Protection

A worker on, or getting on or off, suspended access equipment, must wear a full body harness connected to a fall-arrest system. Safety belts are not allowed with this equipment.

The basic rule is that there must be two independent means of support for each worker on suspended access equipment. That usually means

1) the suspension system of the equipment (suspension lines, climbers, outrigger beams, counterweights, tiebacks, and anchorage), and

2) a fall-arrest system.

These two means of support — suspension system and fall-arrest system — are illustrated in Figure 67.

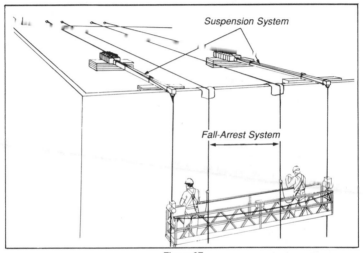

Figure 67
Two Independent Means of Support – Suspension System and Fall-Arrest System

See Figure 21 for components of a fall-arrest system: harnesses, lanyards, rope-grabs, lifelines, and lifeline anchors.

Lifelines

There must be one lifeline for each worker on suspended access equipment. Each lifeline must be securely anchored to an independent support so that failure of the equipment will not cause failure of the lifeline.

Lifelines or lanyards can only be attached directly to suspended access equipment when the equipment has more than one means of support and the failure of one support will not cause failure or collapse of the whole system (Figure 68).

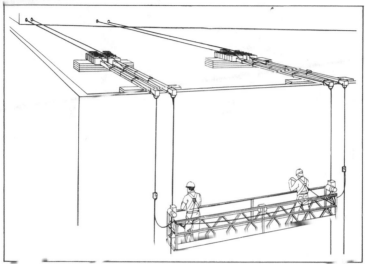

Figure 68
Two Complete Suspension Systems

Two independent means of support can be two complete suspension systems. Lifelines are not required. But workers must still tie off – in this case, to a static line on the stage.

Each lifeline must be
. secured to anchorage that can support ten times the weight of the worker using the line
. anchored separately from other lifelines and from tiebacks for outrigger beams
. protected from abrasion (Figure 69), drifting, and entanglement in traffic or equipment
. anchored perpendicular to the point where the line drops over the edge and at least 3 metres back
. long enough to reach the ground or a working level above ground where the worker can safely get off the equipment
. reasonably taut (loose coils on the roof should be lined out)
. inspected before each use.

Rubber air hose
secured with clamps

Carpet or rubber pad

Figure 69

Adequate anchorage includes
. the bases of large HVAC units
. floor columns
. stub columns on roofs
. designed tieback systems such as eye bolts and rings
. large pipe anchorage systems (12-inch or bigger)
. large masonry chimneys
. roof structures such as mechanical rooms
. parapet clamps attached to reinforced parapet walls on the **other side** of the building.

Never anchor lifelines to
. roof vents or stink pipes
. roof hatches
. small pipes or ducts
. metal chimneys
. lightly constructed parapets
. TV antennas
. stair or balcony railings.

For flame cutting and welding, or work with corrosive chemicals, fibre lifelines are not recommended. Use wire rope lifelines instead. Shock-absorbing lanyards **must** be used with wire rope lifelines.

Common Types

The following types of suspended access equipment are commonly used in construction.

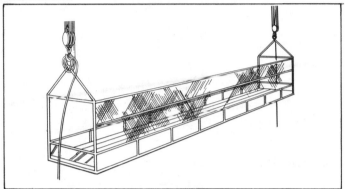

Stage equipped with rope falls (Figure 70)

Limited to structures less than 300 feet high. Useful where the stage must stay in one spot a long time. Not to be used where acid, sandblasting, welding, flame cutting, or other hazards will damage rope.

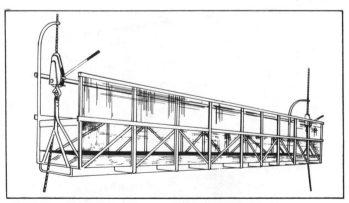

Stage equipped with manual traction climber (Figure 71)

Replaced more and more by equipment with powered climbers. Useful where stage will remain in same position and only limited climbing is required.

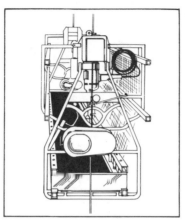

Stage equipped with drill-powered traction climber (Figure 72)

Powered by specially designed electric drills. Operates on 120 volts rather than the 220 commonly required by larger powered climbers but rate of climb is slower. Drills can be removed and stored when not in use to eliminate weather damage and vandalism.

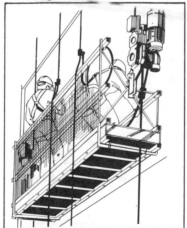

Stage equipped with powered traction climber (Figure 73)

Workhorse of the industry. Fast rate of climb (up to 35ft/min) makes it ideal for large distances and frequent movement. Powered by 220 volts, the unit may require installation of temporary electrical supply.

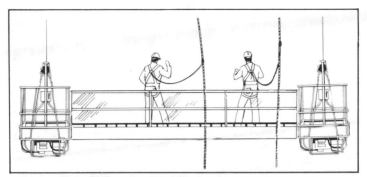

Stage equipped with powered drum hoist climber (Figure 74)

Suspension lines wound on drum do not cross, catch on building, get entangled, or otherwise hinder safe operation.

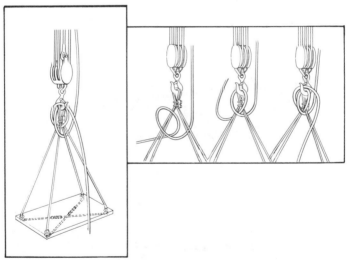

Bosun's chair with rope falls (Figure 75)

For low heights and limited movement. At work level, chair is fixed in position by locking device on block or blackwall's hitch on hook.

Bosun's chair with descent control device (Figure 76)

Useful where workers must descend from level to level in stages. Cannot
be used to climb. Descent control device is simple to rig but should be
reeved with two suspension lines. Since ropes are easily abraded and
damaged, a second line provides added safety.

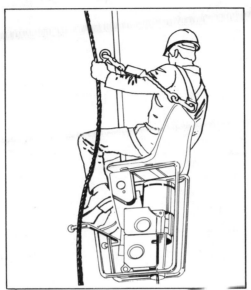

Bosun's chair with powered climber (Figure 77)

Used where considerable travel is required and other equipment would be cumbersome. Compact and generally lighter than work cages.

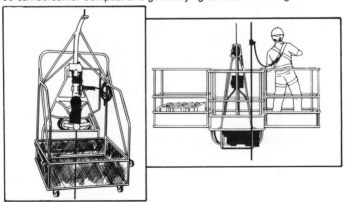

Work cage with powered climber (Figure 78)

Some fold up for easy transport. Can be more safe and efficient than bosun's chairs.

Outrigger Beams

Most are steel, some are aluminum, a few are still wood. Steel beams often come in sections to keep them portable.

Beams must be
— counterweighted to maintain a 4-to-1 safety factor against overturning or failure

— used according to the manufacturer's or supplier's table of counterweights and allowable projections beyond fulcrum for various suspension loads

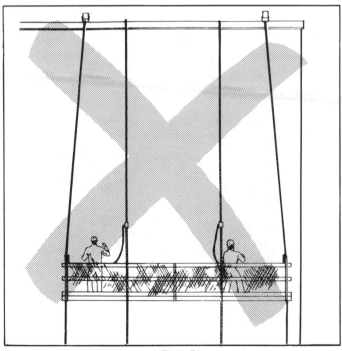

Figure 79
Improper Spacing of Outrigger Beams

- securely tied back to adequate anchorage

- set at right angles to the roof edge wherever possible

- set the same distance apart as stirrups on the stage (Figure 79)

- properly pinned together, with pins wired in position to keep them from loosening and falling out

- free of damage, dings, or kinks

- light enough to be manually handled and transported.

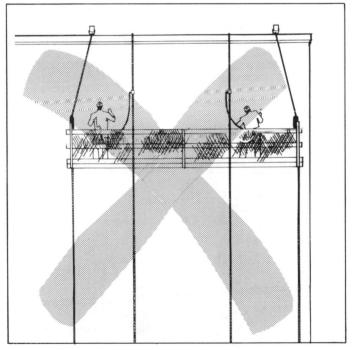

As the stage goes up, the angle of suspension lines increases, causing dangerous side loads.

Platforms

Platforms for suspended scaffolds must be able to support all loads likely to be applied without exceeding the manufacturer's rated working load. For construction we recommend stages with a rating of at least 750 pounds.

Platforms (Figure 80) should be equipped with
- securely attached top rails, mid-rails, and toeboards
- wire mesh from top rail to toeboard
- skid-resistant working surfaces
- properly sized and secured stirrups.

Platforms should be inspected regularly and repaired only by a certified welder with the manufacturer's approval to ensure structural capacity.

Front rails are recomended at all times. They *must* be used where the stage is more than 6 inches away from the structure being worked on.

End rails are usually not required because stirrups and climbers block off ends of the platform.

Wire rope stabilizers attached to stirrups reduce platform sway.

Castors make movement easier on the ground. **Bumper or wall rollers** facilitate movement up and down, provide clearance around small obstacles, and protect the building facade.

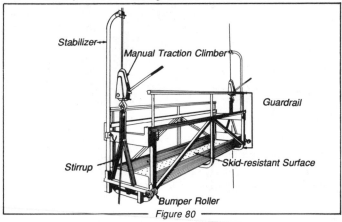

Stabilizer

Manual Traction Climber

Guardrail

Stirrup

Skid-resistant Surface

Bumper Roller

Figure 80

Counterweights

Counterweights range from 50 to 60 pounds and must be
. compatible with outrigger beams
. available in sufficient number to provide the counterweight capacity
  required for beam projection beyond fulcrum
. tied or otherwise secured to the beam so that vibration or movement
  cannot dislodge them (Figure 81).

Bolt on Counterweight
for Slot in Beam

Secured Counterweights
Figure 81

Wire Rope

All wire rope used with suspended access equipment--suspension lines,
tiebacks, static lines--should have a safety factor of 10 against failure
(the manufacturer's catalogue breaking strength).

Suspension Lines

Suspension lines must be
. the type, size, construction, and grade recommended by the climber
  manufacturer
. free of kinks, birdcaging, excessive wear, broken wires, flat spots, and
  other defects.

Make sure that the the solid core wire rope required for some traction
climbers is not replaced by fibre core wire rope, which can be
compressed and slip through the climber.

Tiebacks

Tiebacks should reach from the thimble of the suspension line back
along the outrigger beam, with at least one half-hitch on each section,
loop around the counterweight handles, and extend back to adequate
anchorage (Figure 82).

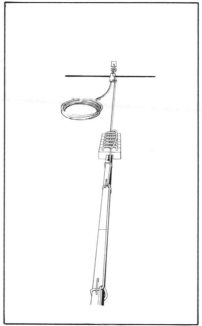

Figure 82

On systems with powered climbers, wire rope is recommended for
tiebacks. On systems with manual climbers, fibre rope is suitable--3/4-
inch polypropylene. On bosun's chairs, tiebacks should be 5/8-inch
polypropylene. Nylon and manila are not recommended.

Wire rope used for tiebacks should be at least equal in size to the wire rope used for the climber.

Cable clips used to fasten wire rope tiebacks should be the right size and number, torqued up tightly, and correctly installed (Figure 83).

Table 6 shows the number of cable clips required for rope sizes commonly used for tiebacks and static lines.

INSTALLATION OF WIRE ROPE CLIPS

Rope Diameter (inches)	Minimum Number of Clips	Amount of Rope Turn Back From Thimble (inches)	Torque in Foot-Pounds Unlubricated Bolts
5/16	3	11-1/2	30
3/8	3	11-1/2	45
7/16	3	11-1/2	65
1/2	3	11-1/2	65
9/16	3	12	95
5/8	3	12	95
3/4	4	18	130
7/8	4	19	225

Table 6

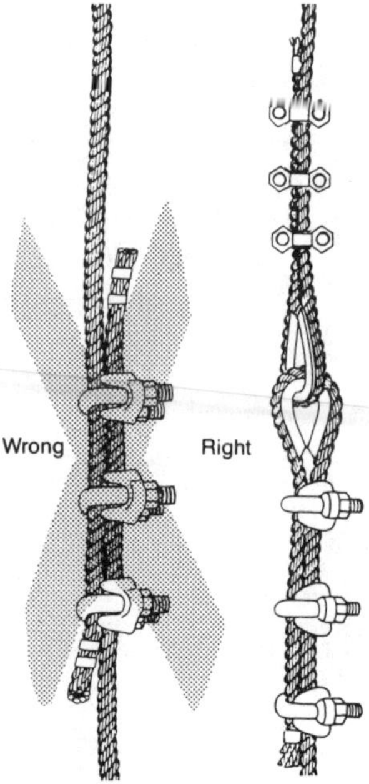

STEP 1

APPLY FIRST CLIP one base width from dead end of wire rope. U-Bolt over dead end. Live end rests in clip saddle. Tighten nuts evenly to recommended torque.

STEP 2

APPLY SECOND CLIP as close to loop as possible. U-Bolt over dead end. Turn nuts firmly but DO NOT TIGHTEN.

STEP 3

APPLY ALL OTHER CLIPS. Space evenly between first two and 6-7 rope diameters apart.

STEP 4

Apply Tension

APPLY TENSION and tighten all nuts to recommended torque.

STEP 5

Apply Tension

CHECK NUT TORQUE after rope has been in operation.

Wrong   Right

Figure 83

118

Polypropylene tiebacks should
- be fitted with a spliced loop and thimble with a safety hook or shackle
- be tied with a round turn and half-hitches, or
- be tied with a triple bowline knot (Figure 84).

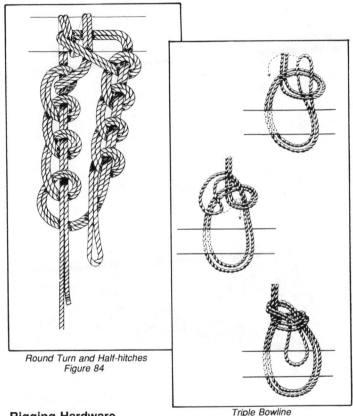

Round Turn and Half-hitches
Figure 84

Triple Bowline

Rigging Hardware

Shackles, hooks, bolts, rings, and other hardware should be
- capable of supporting at least 10 times the maximum load applied
- forged alloy steel
- stamped with a safety factor between 4 and 5 (which must then be divided by 2.5 to ensure a safety factor of 10 for suspended access equipment).

Climbers

Manual traction climbers are usually load-rated for pulling and for hoisting. Use the rating for *hoisting*. Use only the size, type, construction, and grade of wire rope specified by the manufacturer. Leave repairs to an authorized dealer.

A **secondary safety device** (Figure 85) provides protection in case the wire rope connection or primary hoisting system fails. As the device advances up or down, its jaws open slightly to let rope pass through. A sharp downward drop makes the jaws automatically lock with a degree of tightness determined by the load.

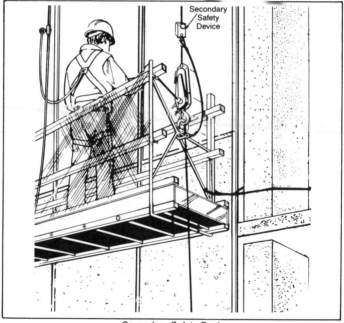

Secondary Safety Device
Figure 85

Most **powered climbers** are driven by electricity (115 or 220 volts). Others are pneumatic or hydraulic. Most have overspeed brakes that engage automatically when descent is too rapid and a manual system for lowering the stage in case of power failure or other emergency. Operators must know how to use these devices.

A powered climber is usually labelled with rated safe working load and climbing speed. Electric climbers may be hampered by voltage drops and overheating if power supplies are inadequate, cables are too small for the length of run, or the run itself is too long. Small climbers carrying loads up near their SWL over large distances may overheat and automatically cut off power.

4-to-1 Safety Factor

Suspended access equipment is subjected to dynamic loads and seldom forgives mistakes in rigging or operation. For these reasons, the outrigger beam/counterweight arrangement must have a safety factor of 4 against overturning or failure.

Suspension Line Load

For **powered climbers**, suspension line load is the manufacturer's rated capacity. The identification plate on the climber should provide this information.

For **manual climbers**, there are two ways of determining suspension line load with suspended stages or bosun's chairs.

Suspended Stages

1) Calculate weight of people, tools, and material plus weight of stage, suspension lines, and climbers.
2) Consider this load to be at least 1,000 pounds.
3) Take 1,000 pounds or the total weight of the system--whichever is **greater**--as the suspension line load.
4) Consider this weight the load on **each** suspension line.

Example	stage	200 lbs
	2 workers	400 lbs
	climbers & suspension lines	200 lbs
	Total	800 lbs
Rig each suspension line for 1,000 pounds.		

Bosun's Chairs

1) Calculate the weight of person, tools, material, chair, suspension line, and climber.
2) Consider this load to be at least 350 pounds.
3) Take 350 pounds or the total weight of the system--whichever is **greater**--as the suspension line load.

How to Calculate Counterweight Load

The first step is to determine suspension line load. For powered climbers, the load is the manufacturer's rated capacity of the climber.

For manual climbers on two-point suspension stages, calculate the weight of people, tools, and material on or suspended from the stage, plus the weight of the stage suspension lines, and climbers.

Consider the load to be at least 1,000 lbs.

Then take 1,000 lbs. or the total weight of the suspended system – whichever is **greater** – as the load on **each** suspension line.

For bosun's chairs with manual climbers, calculate the weight of worker, tools, material, chair, suspension lines, and climber.

Then take this total weight or 350 lbs. – whichever is **greater** – as the suspension line load.

Figure A provides a formula for calculating counterweight load.

We can also look at the problem in terms of what we have working **against** us versus what we need working **for** us.

Working against us are the suspension line load and its distance from the "fulcrum" or tipping point. Working for us are the counterweights and the distance from the tipping point to the centre of the weights (Figure B).

Because of dynamic loads and the unforgiving nature of the equipment, we need to build in a safety factor. The safety factor is 4. We need 4

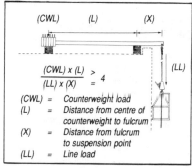

$$\frac{(CWL) \times (L)}{(LL) \times (X)} > = 4$$

(CWL) = Counterweight load
(L) = Distance from centre of counterweight to fulcrum
(X) = Distance from fulcrum to suspension point
(LL) = Line load

Figure A

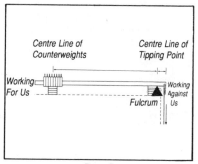

Figure B

122

times as much working for us as we have working against us (Figure C).

A dynamic load is greater than a static load. When we catch something dropped to us, it is heavier than when we simply hold it. This additional dynamic load is one more reason why we need a safety factor.

We have all used a lever to move heavy objects. The longer the lever the easier it is to move the object; or the heavier the person exerting force on the lever, the easier it is to move the object.

Both of these concepts apply to outrigger beams and counterweights.

Equally important is tipping tendency or "moment." This is equal to the load multiplied by the length of the lever.

If we assume our line load is 1,000 lbs. and the projection of the outrigger beam beyond the tipping point is 1 foot (Figure D), the tipping tendency (moment) is:

1,000 x 1 ft. = 1,000 lbs. ft.

This is what we have working against us.

We need to have 4 times this or 4,000 lbs. ft. working for us. If our outrigger beam is 12 feet long, the balance left working for us is:

12 ft. - 1 ft. = 11 ft.

However, we can only consider the distance from fulcrum or tipping point to the **centre** of the counterweights.

Let's say there are 400 lbs. of 50 lb. counterweights, each 1/2 foot wide. In Figure D you can see that the lever arm from the fulcrum can only be 11 ft. - 2 ft. = 9 ft. What we

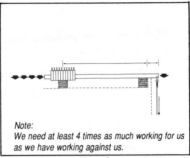

Note:
We need at least 4 times as much working for us as we have working against us.

Figure C

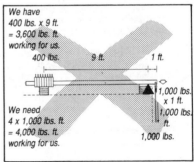

We have
400 lbs. x 9 ft.
= 3,600 lbs. ft.
working for us.

400 lbs.   9 ft.   1 ft.

1,000 lbs. x 1 ft.

We need
4 x 1,000 lbs. ft.
= 4,000 lbs. ft.
working for us.

1,000 lbs. ft.

1,000 lbs.

Inadequate Arrangement
Figure D

have working for us is:

400 lbs. x 9 ft. = 3,600 lbs. ft.

This is less than the 4,000 lbs. ft. we need. We can't change the suspension line load but we can change some of the other factors.

If we reduce the projection of the outrigger beam to 9 inches (.75 ft.), what we have working against us is:

1,000 lbs. x .75 ft. = 0,000 lbs. ft

What we now need working for us is:

4 x 750 = 3,000 lbs. ft.

If we keep the same number of counterweights, what we have working for us is:

400 x 9.25 = 3,700 lbs. ft.

The lever arm is now 9.25 ft. It has gained the 3 inches reduced on the other side of the tipping point (Figure E).

This would be satisfactory since 3,700 lbs. ft. exceeds what we need (3,000 lbs. ft.). Note the difference a few inches can make.

Another approach is to add more counterweights. If we add two more, our counterweights total 500 lbs. However, our lever arm is reduced by 6 inches since the centre of the counterweights has now shifted.

What we have working against us is still the same:

1,000 lbs. x 1 ft. = 1,000 lbs. ft.

What we need working for us is still:

4 x 1,000 lbs. ft. = 4,000 lbs. ft.

What we have working for us is:

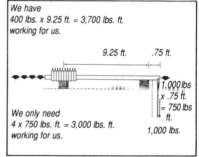

We have
400 lbs. x 9.25 ft. = 3,700 lbs. ft.
working for us.

9.25 ft.   .75 ft.

1,000 lbs
x .75 ft.
= 750 lbs
ft.

We only need
4 x 750 lbs. ft. = 3,000 lbs. ft.
working for us.   1,000 lbs.

Adequate Arrangement
Figure E

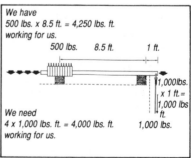

We have
500 lbs. x 8.5 ft. = 4,250 lbs. ft.
working for us.

500 lbs.   8.5 ft.   1 ft.

1,000 lbs.
x 1 ft. =
1,000 lbs
ft.

We need
4 x 1,000 lbs. ft. = 4,000 lbs. ft.   1,000 lbs.
working for us.

Adequate Arrangement
Figure F

500 lbs. x 8.5 ft. = 4,250 lbs. ft.

Again, this would be satisfactory. We have more working for us than we actually need (Figure F).

Additional Considerations

Equipment and material normally found on construction projects can be used to improve set-ups in some situations.

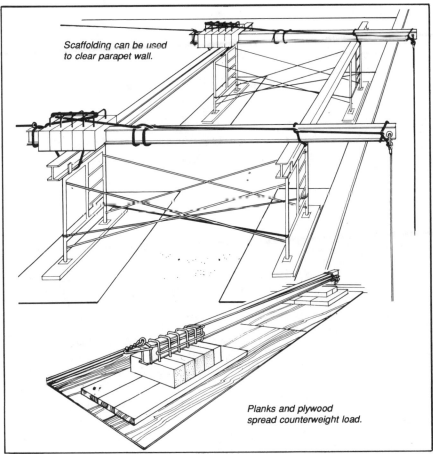

Scaffolding can be used to clear parapet wall.

Planks and plywood spread counterweight load.

Figure 86

12 RIGGING

Tradespeople who are not professional riggers must nonetheless rig
loads at times on the job. Carpenters, for instance, are often involved not
only in handling but in hoisting and landing material. When in doubt
about rigging, consult an experienced rigger or a professional engineer.
Information in this chapter covers only the basics of rigging.

Inspection

Use this checklist to inspect rigging components regularly and before
each lift.

Manila Rope

Manila rope is not recommended for construction use and is illegal for lifelines and
lanyards.

Dusty residue when twisted open	Wear from inside out. Overloading. If extensive, replace rope.
Broken strands, fraying, spongy texture	Replace rope.
Wet	Reduce strength.
Frozen	Thaw and dry at room temperature.
Mildew, dry rot	Replace rope.
Dry and brittle	Do not oil. Wash with cold water and hang in coils to dry.

Polypropylene and Nylon Rope

Chalky exterior appearance	Overexposed to sunlight (UV) rays. Possibly left unprotected outside. Do not use. Discard.
Dusty residue when twisted open	Worn from inside out. If extensive, replace.
Frayed exterior	Abraded by sharp edges. Strength could be reduced.
Broken strands	Destroy and discard.
Cold or frozen	Thaw, dry at room temperature before use.
Size reduction	Usually indicates overloading and excessive wear. Use caution. Reduce capacity accordingly.

Wire Rope (Figure 87)

Rusty, lack of lubrication	Apply light, clean oil. Do not use engine oil.
Excessive outside wear	Used over rough surfaces, with misaligned or wrong sheave sizes. Reduce load capacity according to wear. If outside diameter wire is more than 1/3 worn away, the rope must be replaced.
Broken wires	Up to six allowed in one rope lay or three in one strand in one rope lay with no more than one at an attached fitting. Otherwise, destroy and replace rope.
Crushed, jammed, or flattened strands	Replace rope.
Bulges in rope	Replace, especially non-rotating types.
Gaps between strands	Replace rope.
Core protrusion	Replace rope.
Heat damage, torch burns, or electric arc strikes	Replace rope.
Frozen rope	Do not use. Avoid sudden loading of cold rope.
Kinks, bird-caging	Replace rope. Destroy defective rope.

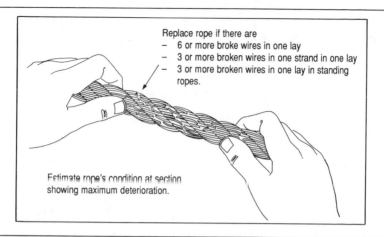

Replace rope if there are
- 6 or more broke wires in one lay
- 3 or more broken wires in one strand in one lay
- 3 or more broken wires in one lay in standing ropes.

Estimate rope's condition at section showing maximum deterioration.

Core protrusion as a result of torsional unbalance created by shock loading.

Protrusion of IWRC resulting from shock loading.

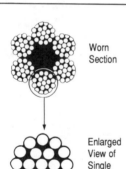

Worn Section

Enlarged View of Single Strand

Where the surface wires are worn by 1/3 or more of their diameter, the rope must be replaced.

Multi-strand rope "bird cages" due to torsional unbalance. Typical of build-up seen at anchorage end of multi-fall crane application.

A "bird cage" caused by sudden release of tension and resultant rebound of rope from overloaded condition. These strands and wires will not return to their original positions.

Figure 87
Wire Rope Inspection

Polypropylene and Nylon Web Slings

Chalky exterior appearance	Overexposed to sunlight (UV) rays. Should be checked by manufacturer.
Frayed exterior	Could have been shock-loaded or abraded. Inspect very carefully for signs of damage.
Breaks, tears, or patches	Destroy. Do not use.
Frozen	Thaw and dry at room temperature before use.
Oil contaminated	Destroy.
Capacity label	Gives capacity of sling when new.

Wire Rope Slings

Broken wires	Up to six allowed in one rope lay or three in one strand in one rope lay with no more than one at an attached fitting. Otherwise, destroy and replace rope.
Kinks, bird-caging	Replace and destroy.
Crushed and jammed strands	Replace and destroy.
Core protrusion	Replace and destroy.
Bulges in rope	Replace and destroy.
Gaps between strands	Replace and destroy.
Wire rope clips	Check proper installation and tightness before each lift. Remember, wire rope stretches when loaded, which may cause clips to loosen.
Attached fittings	Check for broken wires. Replace and destroy if one or more are broken.
Frozen	Do not use. Avoid sudden loading of cold ropes to prevent failure.
Sharp bends	Avoid sharp corners. Use pads such as old carpet, rubber hose, or soft wood to prevent damage.

Chain Slings

Capacity safety tag	Use only alloy steel identified by an "A" or "8" for overhead lifting.
Elongated or stretched links	Return to manufacturer for repair.
Failure to hang straight	Return to manufacturer for repair.
Bent, twisted, or cracked links	Return to manufacturer for repair.
Gouges, chips, or scores	Ground out and reduce capacity according to amount of material removed.

Chain repairs are best left to the manufacturer. Chain beyond repair should be cut with torch into short pieces.

Hardware

Know what hardware to use, how to use it, and how its safe working loads (SWL) compare with the rope or chain used with it.

All fittings must be of adequate strength for the application. Only forged alloy steel load-rated hardware should be used for overhead lifting. Load-rated hardware is stamped with its SWL (Figure 88).

Inspect hardware regularly and before each lift. Telltale signs include
— wear
— cracks
— severe corrosion
— deformation/bends
— mismatched parts
— obvious damage.

Figure 88

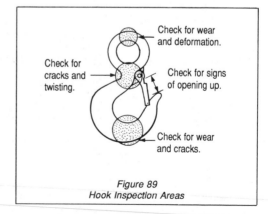

Check for wear and deformation.

Check for cracks and twisting.

Check for signs of opening up.

Check for wear and cracks.

Figure 89
Hook Inspection Areas

Any of these signs indicates a weakened component that should be replaced for safety. Figure 89 shows what to check for on a hook.

Sling Configurations

The term "sling" includes a wide variety of configurations for all fibre ropes, wire ropes, chains, and webs. The most commonly used types in construction are explained here.

Single Vertical Hitch

The total weight of the load is carried by a single leg. This configuration must not be used for lifting loose material, long material, or anything difficult to balance. This hitch provides absolutely no control over the load because it permits rotation.

Bridle Hitch

Two, three, or four single hitches can be used together to form a bridle hitch. They provide excellent stability when the load is distributed equally among the legs, when the hook is directly over the centre of gravity of the load, and the load is raised level. The leg length may need adjustment with turnbuckles to distribute the load.

Single Basket Hitch

This hitch is ideal for loads with inherent stabilizing characteristics. The load is automatically equalized, with each leg supporting half the load. Do not use on loads that are difficult to balance because the load can tilt and slip out of the sling.

Double Basket Hitch

Consists of two single basket hitches passed under the load. The legs of the hitches must be kept far enough apart to provide balance without opening excessive sling angles.

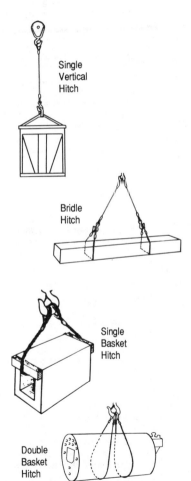

Single
Vertical
Hitch

Bridle
Hitch

Single
Basket
Hitch

Double
Basket
Hitch

131

Double Wrap Basket Hitch

A basket hitch that is wrapped
completely around the load. This
method is excellent for handling loose
materials, pipe, rod, or smooth
cylindrical loads because the rope or
chain exerts a full 360-degree contact
with load and tends to draw it together.

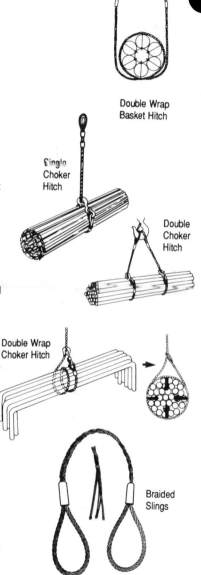

Double Wrap
Basket Hitch

Single Choker Hitch

This forms a noose in the rope and
tightens as the load is lifted. It does not
provide full contact and must not be
used to lift loose bundles or loads
difficult to balance.

Single
Choker
Hitch

Double
Choker
Hitch

Double Choker Hitch

Consists of two single chokers attached
to the load and spread to provide load
stability. Does not grip the load
completely but can balance the load.
Can be used for handling loose
bundles.

Double Wrap
Choker Hitch

Double Wrap Choker Hitch

The rope or chain is wrapped
completely around the load before
being hooked into the vertical part of
the sling. Makes full contact with load
and tends to draw it together.

Braided Slings

Fabricated from six or eight small
diameter ropes braided together to form
a single rope that provides a large
bearing surface, tremendous strength,

Braided
Slings

and flexibility in all directions. They are
very easy to handle and almost
impossible to kink. Especially useful for
basket hitches where low bearing
pressure is desirable or where the bend
is extremely sharp.

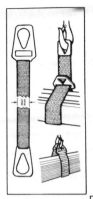

Metal
Mesh
Slings

Metal (Wire or Chain) Mesh Slings

Well adapted for use where loads are
abrasive, hot, or tend to cut fabric or
wire rope slings.

Chain Slings

Made for abrasion and high
temperature resistance. The only chain
suitable for lifting is fabricated from
alloy steel and identified by a letter "A"
or the number "8" or a combination of
the two. Chain must be padded on
sharp corners to prevent bending
stresses.

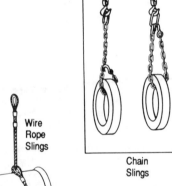

Chain
Slings

Wire Rope Slings

The use of wire rope slings for lifting
materials provides several advantages
over other types of sling. While not as
strong as chain, it has good flexibility
with minimum weight. Breaking outer
wires warn of failure and allow time to
react. Properly fabricated wire rope
slings are very safe for general
construction use.

Wire
Rope
Slings

On smooth surfaces, the basket hitch
should be snubbed against a step or
change of contour to prevent the rope
from slipping as load is applied. The
angle between the load and the sling
should be approximately 60 degrees or
greater to avoid slippage.

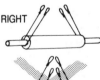

RIGHT

WRONG

Legs will
slide together.

On wooden boxes or crates, the rope will dig into the wood sufficiently to prevent slippage. On other rectangular loads, the rope should be protected by guards or load protectors at the edges to prevent kinking.

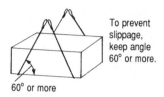

To prevent slippage, keep angle 60° or more.

60° or more

Loads should not be allowed to turn or slide along the rope during a lift. The sling or the load may become scuffed or damaged. Use a double choker if the load must turn.

Turning Load with Double Wrap Choker

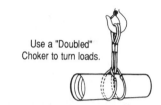

Use a "Doubled" Choker to turn loads.

"Doubled" Choker

The double wrap choker is made by placing both eyes of the sling on top of the load — with the eyes pointing in the direction opposite to the direction of turn. The centre of the sling is passed around the load, through both eyes, and up to the hook. This hitch provides complete control over the load during the entire turning operation. The load automatically equalizes between the two supporting legs of the sling. Because the load is turned into a tight sling, there is no movement between the load and the sling.

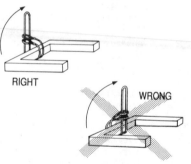

RIGHT

WRONG

If the double wrap choker is incorrectly made and the two eyes are placed on the crane hook, the supporting legs of the sling may not be equal in length and the load may be carried by one leg only.

Two- or four-ends down hitches must be used cautiously because the cable may slide through the hook as the weight of the load is redistributed. Control by tying one end of the load back to the hook to fix the rope position.

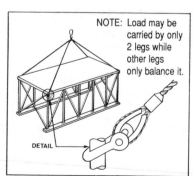

NOTE: Load may be carried by only 2 legs while other legs only balance it.

DETAIL

WIRE ROPE SLINGS
6 x 19 Classification Group, Improved Plow Steel, Fibre Core

Rope Diameter (Inches)	Single Vertical Hitch	Single Choker Hitch	Single Basket Hitch (Vertical Legs)	2-Leg Bridle Hitch & Single Basket Hitch With Legs Inclined		
				60°	45°	30°
3/16	600	450	1,200	1,050	850	600
1/4	1,100	825	2,200	1,900	1,550	1,100
5/16	1,650	1,250	3,300	2,850	2,350	1,650
3/8	2,400	1,800	4,800	4,150	3,400	2,400
7/16	3,200	2,400	6,400	5,550	4,500	3,200
1/2	4,400	3,300	8,800	7,600	6,200	4,400
9/16	5,300	4,000	10,600	9,200	7,500	5,300
5/8	6,600	4,950	13,200	11,400	9,350	6,600
3/4	9,500	7,100	19,000	16,500	13,400	9,500
7/8	12,800	9,600	25,600	22,200	18,100	12,800
1	16,700	12,500	33,400	28,900	23,600	16,700
1 1/8	21,200	15,900	42,400	36,700	30,000	21,200
1 1/4	26,200	19,700	52,400	45,400	37,000	26,200
1 3/8	32,400	24,300	64,800	56,100	45,800	32,400
1 1/2	38,400	28,800	76,800	66,500	54,300	38,400
1 5/8	45,200	33,900	90,400	78,300	63,900	45,200
1 3/4	52,000	39,000	104,000	90,000	73,500	52,000
1 7/8	60,800	45,600	121,600	105,300	86,000	60,800
2	67,600	50,700	135,200	117,100	95,600	67,600
2 1/4	84,000	63,000	168,000	145,500	118,800	84,000
2 1/2	104,000	78,000	208,000	180,100	147,000	104,000
2 3/4	122,000	91,500	244,000	211,300	172,500	122,000

MAXIMUM SAFE WORKING LOADS — POUNDS (Safety Factor = 5)

If used with Choker Hitch multiply above values by 3/4.

Note: Table values are for slings with eyes and thimbles in both ends, Flemish Spliced Eyes and mechanical sleeves.
Eyes formed by cable clips — reduce loads by 20%.

NYLON WEB SLINGS

	6800 lb/in Material					
	Maximum Safe Working Loads—Pounds (Safety Factor = 5) (Eye & Eye, Twisted Eye, Triangle Fittings, Choker Fittings)					
Web Width (Inches)	Single Vertical Hitch	Single Choker Hitch	Single Basket Hitch (Vertical Legs)	2-Leg Bridle Hitch & Single Basket Hitch With Legs Inclined		
				60°	45°	30°
1	1,100	825	2,200	1,905	1,555	1,100
2	2,200	1,650	4,400	3,810	3,110	2,200
3	3,300	2,475	6,600	5,715	4,665	3,300
4	4,400	3,300	8,800	7,620	6,220	4,400
5	5,500	4,125	11,000	9,525	7,775	5,500
6	6,600	4,950	13,200	11,430	9,330	6,600

If used with Choker Hitch multiply above values by ¾.

1. For safe working loads of endless or grommet slings, multiply above values by 2.
2. Values have been adjusted to reflect fabrication efficiency (FE) using formulas and tables developed by the Web Sling Association. This accounts for strength loss due to stitching and manufacture.
3. All web slings must carry a load rating tag as specified in OH&S Regulations.

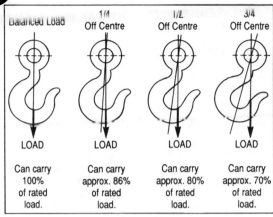

Balanced Load	1/4 Off Centre	1/2 Off Centre	3/4 Off Centre
LOAD	LOAD	LOAD	LOAD
Can carry 100% of rated load.	Can carry approx. 86% of rated load.	Can carry approx. 80% of rated load.	Can carry approx. 70% of rated load.

Figure 91
Point Loading

LOAD
Can Carry approx 40% of rated load.

Figure 90
Effect of Eccentric Loads on Hook Capacity

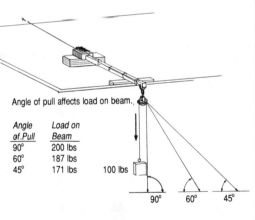

Angle of pull affects load on beam.

Angle of Pull	Load on Beam
90°	200 lbs
60°	187 lbs
45°	171 lbs

100 lbs

Figure 93
Effect of Pull Angle on Beam Load

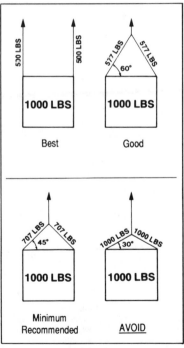

Best

Good

Minimum Recommended

AVOID

Figure 92
Effect of Sling Angle on Sling Load

137

Hooking Up

- Avoid sharp bends, pinching, and kinks in rigging equipment. Thimbles should be used at all times in sling eyes.
- Never wrap a wire rope sling completely around a hook. The tight radius will damage the sling.
- Make sure the load is balanced in the hook. Eccentric loading can reduce capacity dangerously (Figure 90).
- Never point-load a hook unless it is designed and rated for such use (Figure 91).
- Never wrap the crane hoist rope around the load. Attach the load to the hook by slings or other rigging devices adequate for the load.
- Avoid bending the eye section of wire rope slings around corners. The band will weaken the splice or swaging.
- Avoid bending wire rope slings near any attached fitting.
- Understand the effect of sling angle on sling load (Figure 92) and pull angle on beam load (Figure 93).

Rig the load with its centre of gravity directly below the hook to ensure stability. The crane hook should be brought over the load's centre of gravity before the lift is started. Crane hook and load line should be vertical before lifting. Weights of common materials are listed in Tables 7-11.

Basic Knots and Hitches

Every worker should be able to tie the basic knots and hitches that are useful in everyday work.

Round Turn and Two Half Hitches

Used to secure loads to be hoisted horizontally. Two are usually required because the load can slide out if lifted vertically.

Round Turn and Two Half Hitches

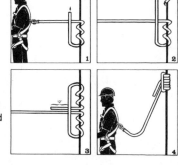

Triple Sliding Hitch

Used for tying off to a lifeline. Every worker must know this hitch as it is a critical component for fall protection.

Timber Hitch and Two Half Hitches

A good way to secure a scaffold plank for hoisting vertically. The timber hitch grips the load.

Reef or Square Knot

Can be used for tying two ropes of the same diameter together. It is unsuitable for wet or slippery ropes and should be used with caution since it unties easily when either free end is jerked. Both live and dead ends of the rope must come out of the loops at the same side.

Two Half Hitches

Two half hitches, which can be quickly tied, are reliable and can be put to almost any general use.

Running Bowline

The running bowline is mainly used for hanging objects with ropes of different diameters. The weight of the object determines the tension necessary for the knot to grip.

Make an overhand loop with the end of the rope held toward you (1). Hold the loop with your thumb and fingers and bring the standing part of the rope back so that it lies behind the loop (2).
Take the end of the rope in behind the standing part, bring it up, and feed it through the loop (3). Pass it behind the standing part at the top of the loop and bring it back down through the loop (4).

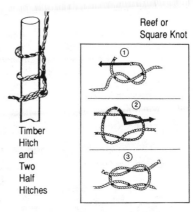

Timber
Hitch
and
Two
Half
Hitches

Reef or
Square Knot

Two
Half
Hitches

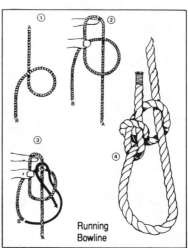

Running
Bowline

Bowline

Never jams or slips when properly tied. It is a universal knot if properly tied and untied. Two interlocking bowlines can be used to join two ropes together. Single bowlines can be used for hoisting or hitching directly around a ring or post.

Sheet Bend

Can be used for tying ropes of light or medium size.

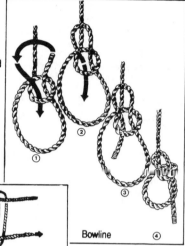

Bowline ④

Single Sheet Bend

Double Sheet Bend

WEIGHTS OF MATERIALS (Based On Volume)			
Material	Approximate Weight Lbs. Per Cubic Foot	Material	Approximate Weight Lbs. Per Cubic Foot
METALS		**TIMBER, AIR-DRY**	
Aluminum	165	Cedar	22
Brass	535	Fir, Douglas, seasoned	34
Bronze	500	Fir, Douglas, unseasoned	40
Copper	560	Fir, Douglas, wet	50
Iron	480	Fir, Douglas, glue laminated	34
Lead	710	Hemlock	30
Steel	490	Pine	30
Tin	460	Poplar	30
MASONRY		Spruce	28
Ashlar masonry	140-160	**LIQUIDS**	
Brick masonry, soft	110	Alcohol, pure	49
Brick masonry, common (about		Gasoline	42
3 tons per thousand)	125	Oils	58
Brick masonry, pressed	140	Water	62
Clay tile masonry, average	60	**EARTH**	
Rubble masonry	130-155	Earth, wet	100
Concrete, cinder, haydite	100-110	Earth, dry (about 2050 lbs.	
Concrete, slag	130	per cu. yd.)	75
Concrete, stone	144	Sand and gravel, wet	120
Concrete, stone, reinforced		Sand and gravel, dry	105
(4050 lbs. per cu. yd.)	150	River sand (about 3240 lbs.	
ICE AND SNOW		per cu. yd.)	120
Ice	56	**VARIOUS BUILDING**	
Snow, dry, fresh fallen	8	**MATERIALS**	
Snow, dry, packed	12-25	Cement, portland, loose	94
Snow, wet	27-40	Cement, portland, set	183
MISCELLANEOUS		Lime, gypsum, loose	53-64
Asphalt	80	Mortar, cement-lime, set	103
Tar	75	Crushed rock (about 2565 lbs.	
Glass	160	per cu. yd.)	90-110
Paper	60		

Table 7

Table 8

DRYWALL—WEIGHTS			
Non-Fire Rated	8'	10'	12'
1/2"	58 lbs.	72 lbs.	86 lbs.
5/8"	74 lbs.	92 lbs.	110 lbs.
Fire-Rated			
1/2"	64 lbs.	80 lbs.	96 lbs.
5/8"	77 lbs.	96 lbs.	115 lbs.

STEEL STUDS AND TRIMS—WEIGHTS		Pcs./Bdl.	Lbs. (per 1,000 Lin. Ft).
STUD SIZE—.018 THICKNESS			
1 5/8	All Lengths	10	290
2 1/2	All Lengths	10	340
3 5/8	All Lengths	10	415
6 (.020)	All Lengths	10	625
TRACK SIZES—.018 THICKNESS			
1 5/8	Regular Leg	10	240
2 1/2	Regular Leg	10	295
3 5/8	Regular Leg	10	365
6 (.020)	Regular Leg	10	570
1 5/8	2 Leg	12	365
2 1/2	2 Leg	6	415
3 5/8	2 Leg	6	470
DRYWALL FURRING CHANNEL			
Electro-Galvanized		10	300
DRYWALL CORNER BEAD			
1 1/4 x 1 1/4		Various	120
RESILIENT CHANNEL			
Electro-Galvanized		20	210
DRYWALL TRIMS			
1/2 Door & Window L.		20	100
5/8 Door & Window L.		20	100
3/8 Casing Bead J.		20	110
1/2 Casing Bead J.		20	120
5/8 Casing Bead J.		20	130
DRYWALL ANGLE			
1 x 2 Drywall Angle		10	200

Table 9

141

WEIGHTS OF MATERIALS (Based on Surface Area)

Material	Approximate Weight Lbs. Per Square Foot
CEILINGS	
(Per Inch of Thickness)	
Plaster board	5
Acoustic and fire resistive tile	2
Plaster, gypsum-sand	8
Plaster, light aggregate	4
Plaster, cement sand	12
ROOFING	
Three-ply felt and gravel	5.5
Five-ply felt and gravel	6.5
Three-ply felt, no gravel	3
Five-ply felt, no gravel	4
Shingles, wood	2
Shingles, asbestos	3
Shingles, asphalt	2.5
Shingles, 1/4 inch slate	10
Shingles, tile	14
PARTITIONS	
Steel partitions	4
Solid 2" gypsum-sand plaster	20
Solid 2" gypsum-light agg. plaster	12
Metal studs, metal lath, 3/4" plaster both sides	18

Material	Approximate Weight Lbs. Per Square Foot
FLOORING	
(Per Inch of Thickness)	
Hardwood	5
Sheathing	2.5
Plywood, fir	3
Wood block, treated	4
Concrete, finish or fill	12
Mastic base	12
Mortar base	10
Terrazzo	12.5
Tile, vinyl 1/8 inch	1.5
Tile, linoleum 3/16 inch	1
Tile, cork, per 1/16 inch	0.5
Tile, rubber or asphalt 3/16 inch	2
Tile, ceramic or quarry 3/4 inch	11
Carpeting	2
DECKS AND SLABS	
Steel roof deck 1 1/2" — 14 ga.	5
— 16 ga.	4
— 18 ga.	3
— 20 ga.	2.5
— 22 ga.	2
Steel cellular deck 1 1/2" — 12/12 ga.	11

Metal or wood studs, plaster board and 1/2" plaster both sides	18
Plaster 1/2"	4
Hollow clay tile 2 inch	13
3 inch	16
4 inch	18
5 inch	20
6 inch	25
Hollow slag concrete block 4 inch	24
6 inch	35
Hollow gypsum block 3 inch	10
4 inch	13
5 inch	15.5
6 inch	16.5
Solid gypsum block 2 inch	9.5
3 inch	13

MASONRY WALLS
(Per 4 Inch of Thickness)

Brick	40
Glass brick	20
Hollow concrete block	30
Hollow slag concrete block	24
Hollow cinder concrete block	20
Hollow haydite block	22
Stone, average	55
Bearing hollow clay tile	23

—14/14 ga.	8
—16/16 ga.	6.5
—18/18 ga.	5
—20/20 ga.	3.5
Steel cellular deck 3" —12/12 ga.	12.5
—14/14 ga.	9.5
—16/16 ga.	7.5
—18/18 ga.	6
—20/20 ga.	4.5
Concrete, reinforced, per inch	12.5
Concrete, gypsum, per inch	5
Concrete, lightweight, per inch	5-10

MISCELLANEOUS

Windows, glass, frame	8
Skylight, glass, frame	12
Corrugated asbestos 1/4 inch	3.5
Glass, plate 1/4 inch	3.5
Glass, common	1.5
Plastic sheet 1/4 inch	1.5
Corrugated steel sheet, galv. —12 ga.	5.5
—14 ga.	4
—16 ga.	3
—18 ga.	2.5
—20 ga.	2
—22 ga.	1.5
Wood Joists — 16" ctrs. 2 x 12	3.5
2 x 10	3
2 x 8	2.5
Steel plate (per inch of thickness)	40

Table 10

SUSPENDED CEILING GRID SYSTEMS—WEIGHTS

Systems	Qty./Ctn. (Lin. Ft.)	Lbs./Ctn. (Lbs.)
NON-FIRE RATED GRID SYSTEM		
1 1/2 x 144" Main Runner	240	58
1 x 48" Cross Tee	300	55
1 x 24" Cross Tee	150	28
1 x 30" Cross Tee	187.5	35
1 x 20" Cross Tee	125	23
1 x 12" Cross Tee	75	14
FIRE-RATED GRID SYSTEM		
1 1/2 x 144" Main Runner	240	70
1 1/2 x 48" Cross Tee	240	70
1 1/2 x 24" Cross Tee	120	35
WALL MOULDINGS		
Wall Mould 3/4 x 15/16 x 120"	400	49
Reveal Mould 3/4 x 3/4 x 1/2 x 3/4 x 120"	200	36
ACCESSORIES		
Hold-Down Clips (for 5/8" tile)	500 pcs.	3
BASKETWEAVE & CONVENTIONAL **5' x 5' MODULE—NON RATED**		
1 1/2 x 120" Main Member	200	49
1 1/2 x 60" Cross Tee	250	61
Wall Mould 3/4 x 15/16 x 120"	400	57
THIN LINE GRID SYSTEM—NON-RATED		
Main Runner 1 1/2 x 144"	300	65
Cross Tee 1 1/2 x 48"	300	65
Cross Tee 1 1/2 x 24"	150	33
Wall Mould 15/16 x 9/16 x 120"	500	62
Reveal Mould 1 x 3/8 x 3/8 x 9/16 x 120"	300	48
Main Runner 1 1/12 x 144"	300	65
Cross Tee 1 1/2 x 48"	300	65
Cross Tee 1 1/2 x 24"	150	33
Wall Mould 15/16 x 9/16 x 120"	500	62

Table 11

HAND SIGNALS FOR HOISTING OPERATIONS

Load Up 1	**Load Down** 2	**Load Up Slowly** 3	**Load Down Slowly** 4	**Boom Up** 5	**Boom Down** 6
Boom Up Slowly 7	**Boom Down Slowly** 8	**Boom Up Load Down** 9	**Boom Down Load Up** 10	**Everything Slowly** 11	**Use Whip Line** 12
Use Main Line 13	**Travel Forward** 14	**Turn Right** 15	**Turn Left** 16	**Shorten Hydraulic Boom** 17	**Extend Hydraulic Boom** 18
Swing Load 19	**Stop** 20	**Close Clam** 21	**Open Clam** 22	**Dog Everything** 23	No response should be made to unclear signals.

145

Hazards

13 ELECTRICAL HAZARDS

Most tradespeople tend to take electricity for granted as a steady, reliable source of power for a wide variety of tools, equipment, and operations. But familiarity can create a false sense of security. Remember that electricity is *always* a potential source of danger.

> The basic rule is straightforward: Consider all electrical wires and equipment live until they are tested and proven otherwise.

Other guidelines are provided under the following headings.

Panels

- Temporary panel boards (Figure 93) must be securely mounted, protected from weather and water, accessible to workers, and kept clear of obstructions.

- Use only fuses or breakers of the recommended amperage.

- Follow regulated procedures for tagging and lockout. Section 188 of the *Regulations for Construction Projects* specifies conditions and controls.

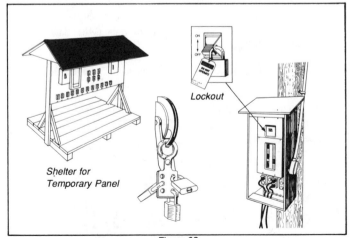

Lockout

Shelter for Temporary Panel

Figure 93

Cords and Plugs

- Never cut off, bend back, or cheat the ground pin on three-prong plugs.

- Make sure that plugs and cords are in good condition.

- Make sure that extension cords are the right gauge for the job to prevent overheating, voltage drops, and tool burnout.

- Check extension cords and outlets with a circuit-tester (Figure 94) before use.

- Use cords fitted with deadfront plugs (Figure 95). These present less risk of shock and shortcircuit than open front plugs.

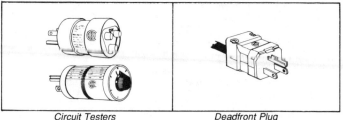

Circuit Testers   Deadfront Plug
Figure 94   Figure 95

- Do not use extension or tool cords that are defective or have been improperly repaired.

- Do not wire plugs into outlets. Disconnecting will take too long in an emergency.

- Protect cords from traffic. Protect bulbs with cages (Figure 96).

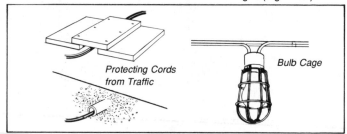

Protecting Cords
from Traffic

Bulb Cage

Figure 96

Temporary Lighting

- Avoid contact with the wires strung for temporary lighting. Frequent relocation of circuits can loosen connections, break insulation, and create other hazards.

- Beware of tripping and shock hazards from stringers overhead and underfoot (Figure 97).

- Do not use temporary lighting circuits as extension cords. If a fuse blows, it can be dangerous to find your way to the panel in the dark.

- Take care that exposed wires do not contact steel door frames in the final stages of work, when temporary lines often pass through doors that may be accidentally closed on them (Figure 98).

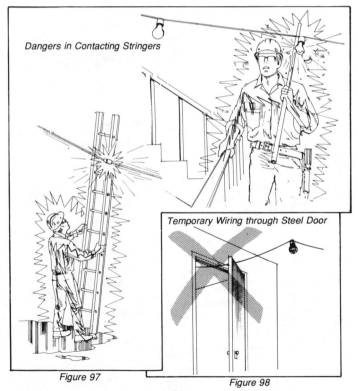

Dangers in Contacting Stringers

Temporary Wiring through Steel Door

Figure 97

Figure 98

- Replace missing or burned-out bulbs to maintain required levels of illumination in stairwells, basements, halls, and other areas.

Tools

- Use only tools that are grounded or double-insulated.

- Make sure the casings of double-insulated tools are not cracked or broken.

- Always use a ground fault circuit interrupter (GFCI) with any portable electric tool operated outdoors or in wet locations (Figure 99). This is required by the *Regulations for Construction Projects*, Section 192. GFCIs detect current leaking to ground from tool or cord and shut off power before injury or damage can occur.

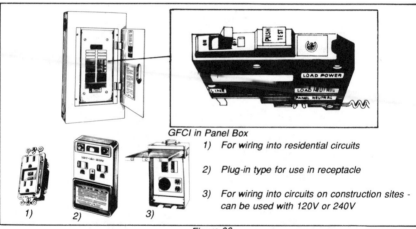

GFCI in Panel Box

1) For wiring into residential circuits

2) Plug-in type for use in receptacle

3) For wiring into circuits on construction sites - can be used with 120V or 240V

Figure 99
Ground Fault Circuit Interrupters

Insulated Handles and Grips

Eye Protection

Insulated Gloves

CSA-Certified Shock-Resistant Boots

Figure 100

- Use hand tools with insulated handles and grips. Whenever required, wear protective equipment--safety goggles, insulated gloves, shock-resistant footwear (Figure 100).

- Do not hold water pipes or other grounded conductors when using electric tools. A defect in tool or cord will make you part of the circuit, causing shock, a fall off your ladder, or, at worst, electrocution.

- Before drilling, hammering, or cutting with hand or power tools, check for electrical wires or equipment behind walls, above ceilings, and under floors.

- Keep cords out of the path of electric tools and equipment.

- Before making adjustments or changing attachments, disconnect electric tools from the power source. Switching off the tool may not be enough to prevent accidental startup.

- Never bypass broken switches on tools or equipment by plugging and unplugging the cord. Shutting off power will take too long in an emergency.

- Any shock or tingle, no matter how slight, means that the tool or equipment should be checked and repaired if necessary.

- Never use metal or metal-reinforced ladders near live wires or equipment. Use wooden or fibreglass ladders.

Powerlines

- Locate all underground and overhead services before starting work. Determine voltage of electrical utilities.

- Have powerlines moved, insulated, or de-energized where necessary.

- Mark underground lines on all plans and drawings. Post warning signs along their route.

- Avoid storing material or equipment under powerlines. If it must be stored there, hang warning flags and signs to prevent other workers from using hoisting equipment to move or lift it.

- With backhoes, cranes, and similar equipment near powerlines, use a signaller to warn the operator when any part of the equipment or load approaches the minimum allowable distances.

Voltage Rating of Powerline	Minimum Distance
750 to 150,000 volts	3 metres (10')
150,001 to 250,000 volts	4.6 metres (15')
over 250,000 volts	6 metres (20')

- Before moving ladders, rolling scaffolds, or elevating work platforms, always check for overhead wires. Death and injury have been caused by electrical contact with access equipment (Figure 101).

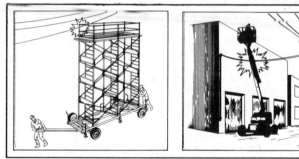

Figure 101.

Shock

The passage of electricity through the body is called shock. Effects can range from a tingling sensation to death. A shock that may not be enough to kill or even injure can nonetheless startle a worker and cause a fall from a ladder or work platform.

Burns are the most common shock-related injury. Electricity can cause severe burns at points of entry and exit. The damage is often more serious than it looks. Although entry and exit wounds may be small, bone and muscle can be extensively burned in between.

Shock can also cause irregular beating of the heart (fibrillation) leading to respiratory failure and cardiac arrest.

The effect of electric shock on the body is determined by three main factors:
1) how much current is flowing through the body (measured in amperes and determined by voltage and resistance)
2) the path of current through the body
3) how long the body is in the circuit.

Table 12 shows generally how degree of injury relates to amount of current passing through a body for a few seconds.

In addition to emergency procedures (Figure 1) and artificial respiration (Figure 4), workers should know what to do in the event of unbroken electrical contact (Figure 102).

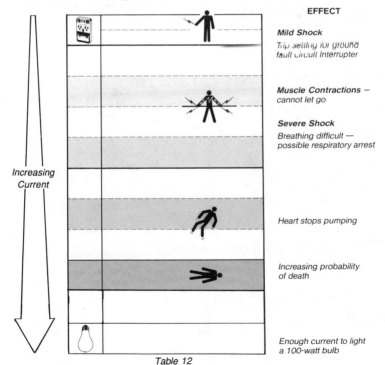

EFFECT

Mild Shock
Trip setting for ground fault circuit interrupter

Muscle Contractions –
cannot let go

Severe Shock
Breathing difficult —
possible respiratory arrest

Increasing Current

Heart stops pumping

Increasing probability of death

Enough current to light a 100-watt bulb

Table 12

155

Procedure for Unbroken Contact

1 In some electrical accidents, the injured or unconscious person remains in contact with the live wire or equipment.

Rescue should only be attempted after power has been turned off.

2 In some cases of low voltage, when power cannot be turned off, break contact if possible. Use a dry board, rubber hose, or dry polypropylene rope to move either the injured person or the line.

An object can sometimes be thrown to separate the injured person from the wire.

If you don't know the voltage, treat it as **high**.

3 **WARNING**: Even with dry wood or rubber, touching the injured person can be dangerous. High voltage can jump a considerable gap and objects that are normally insulators may become conductors.

Only electrical personnel specially trained and equipped to use special live-line tools can attempt rescue safely.

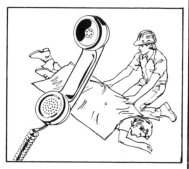

4 Call emergency services — in most cases, ambulance, fire department, and utility.

WARNING: Give first aid only after the injured person is free of contact.

Figure 102

156

14 TRENCHING

Each year, Ontario averages 3 to 4 fatalities and about 350 lost-time injuries directly related to trenching.

Trenching fatalities are mainly caused by cave-ins. Death occurs by suffocation or crushing when a worker is buried by falling soil.

The following are the main causes of trenching lost-time injuries:

— material falling into the trench
— handling and placing material
— falls as workers climb in or out
— falling over equipment or excavated material
— falling into the trench
— exposure to toxic, irritating, or flammable gases.

Causes of Cave-Ins

Soil properties often vary widely from the top to the bottom and along the length of a trench.

Many factors such as cracks, water, vibration, weather, and previous excavation can affect trench stability (Figure 100). Time is also a critical factor. Some trenches will remain open for a long period, then suddenly collapse for no apparent reason.

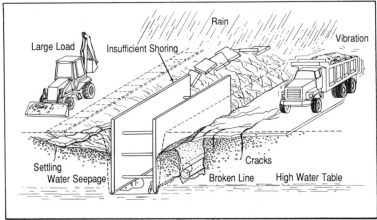

Figure 103
Many factors affect trench stability.

157

Figure 104 shows the typical causes of cave-ins. The main factors affecting trench stability are soil type, moisture, vibration, surcharge, previous excavation, existing foundations, and weather.

Soil Type

Type of soil determines the strength and stability of trench walls.

The *Regulations for Construction Projects* describe four general types of soil from dry, dense, and hard (Type 1) to wet, muddy, and unable to support itself (Type 4).

Identifying soil types requires knowledge, skill, and experience. Even hard soil may contain faults in seams or layers that make it unstable when excavated. Supervision must be aware of the soil types to be encountered during a job and plan protection accordingly.

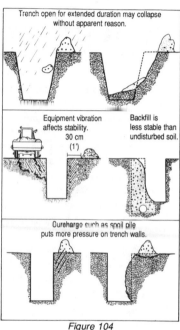

Figure 104

Moisture Content

The amount of moisture in the soil has a great effect on soil strength.

Once a trench is dug, the sides of the open excavation are exposed to the air. Moisture content of the soil begins to change almost immediately and the strength of the walls may be affected.

The longer an excavation is open to the
air, the greater the risk of cave-in.

Vibration

Vibration from various sources can affect trench strength.

Often trench walls are subject to vibration from vehicular traffic or from
construction operations such as earth moving, compaction, pile driving,
and blasting. These can all contribute to the collapse of trench walls.

Surcharge

A surcharge is an excessive load or weight that can affect trench
stability.
For instance, excavated soil piled next to the trench can exert pressure
on the walls. Placement of spoil piles is therefore important. Spoil should
be kept as far as practical from the edge of the trench. Mobile equipment
and other material stored close to the trench also add a surcharge that
will affect trench stability.

One metre from the edge to the toe of the spoil pile is the minimum
requirement. The distance should be greater for deeper trenches.

Previous Excavation

Old utility trenches either crossing or
running parallel to the new trench can
affect the strength and stability (Figure
105).Soil around and between these old
excavations is very unstable. At best it
is considered Type 3 soil – that is,
loose, soft, and low in internal strength.
In some unusual circumstances it may
be Type 4 – wet, muddy, and unable to
support itself.

*Old utilities are surrounded by backfilled
soil which is usually less stable than
undisturbed soil.*

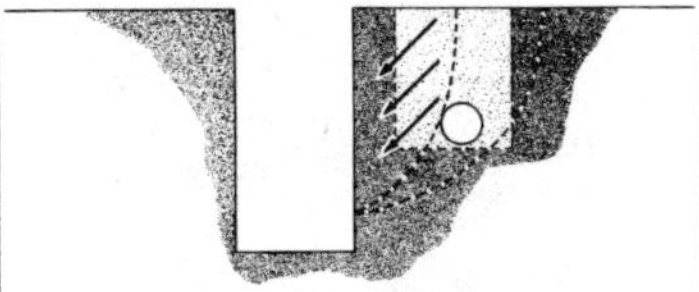

Figure 105

This kind of soil will not stand up unless

159

it is sloped or shored.

Existing Foundations

Around most trenches and excavations there is a failure zone where surcharges, changes in soil condition, or other disruptions can cause collapse.

When the foundation of a building adjacent to the trench or excavation extends into this failure zone, the result can be a cave-in (Figure 106). Soil in this situation is usually considered Type 3.

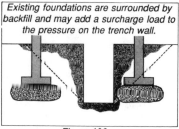

Existing foundations are surrounded by backfill and may add a surcharge load to the pressure on the trench wall.

Figure 106

Weather

Rain, melting snow, thawing earth, and overflow from adjacent streams, storm drains, and sewers all produce changes in soil conditions. In fact, water from any source can increase the rate of seepage and reduce soil cohesion.

Don't make frozen soil an excuse for heavier loading or reduced shoring. Frost extends to a limited depth only.

Protection Against Cave-Ins

There are three basic methods of protecting workers against trench cave-ins:
— sloping
— trench boxes
— shoring.

Most fatal cave-ins occur on small jobs of short duration such as service connections and excavations for drains and wells. Too often people think that these jobs are not hazardous enough to require safeguards against collapse.

Sloping

One way to ensure that a trench will not collapse is to slope the walls. Where space and other requirements permit sloping, the angle of slope depends on soil conditions (Figure 107).

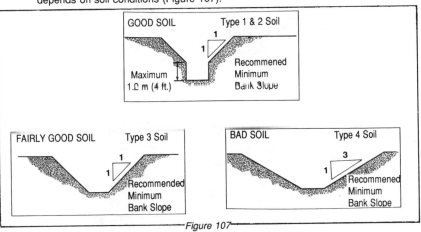

Figure 107

It is good practice to cut a bench at top of shoring or trench box (Figure 108).

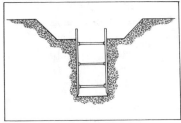

Figure 108

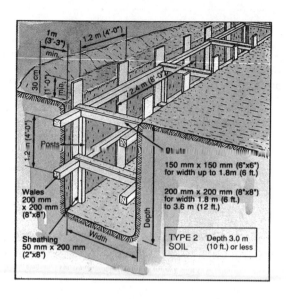

1m (3'-3") min.

1.2 m (4'-0")

30 cm (1'-0") min.

2.4 m (8'-0")

1.2 m (4'-0")

Posts

Wales
200 mm
x 200 mm
(8"x8")

Sheathing
50 mm x 200 mm
(2"x8")

Width

Depth

150 mm x 150 mm (6"x6")
for width up to 1.8m (6 ft.)

200 mm x 200 mm (8"x8")
for width 1.8 m (6 ft.)
to 3.6 m (12 ft.)

TYPE 2   Depth 3.0 m
SOIL   (10 ft.) or less

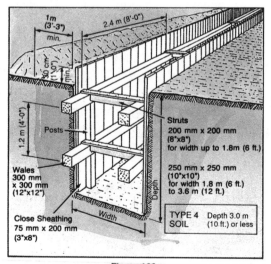

1m (3'-3") min.

2.4 m (8'-0")

30 cm (1'-0")

1.2 m (4'-0")

Posts

Wales
300 mm
x 300 mm
(12"x12")

Close Sheathing
75 mm x 200 mm
(3"x8")

Width

Depth

Struts
200 mm x 200 mm
(8"x8")
for width up to 1.8m (6 ft.)

250 mm x 250 mm
(10"x10")
for width 1.8 m (6 ft.)
to 3.6 m (12 ft.)

TYPE 4   Depth 3.0 m
SOIL   (10 ft.) or less

Figure 109

162

Trench Boxes

Trench boxes are not usually intended to shore up or otherwise support trench walls. They are meant to protect workers in case of a cave-in. They are capable of supporting trench walls if the space between the box and the trench wall is backfilled.

As long as workers are in the trench they should remain inside the box and leave only when the box is being moved. A ladder should be set up in the trench box at all times.

Shoring

Shoring is a system which "shores" up or supports trench walls to prevent movement of soil, underground utilities, roadways, and foundations.

The two types of shoring most commonly used are timber and hydraulic. Both consist of posts, wales, struts, and sheathing.

Figure 109 identifies components, dimensions and other requirements for timber shoring in typical trenches.

Wherever possible, shoring should be installed as excavation proceeds. If there is a delay between digging and shoring, no one must be allowed to enter the unprotected trench. All shoring should be installed from the top down and removed from the bottom up.

Ladders

Whether protected by sloping, boxes, or shoring, trenches should be provided with ladders so that workers can enter and exit safely (Figure 110).

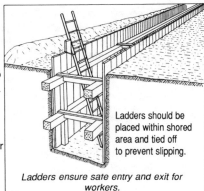

Ladders should be placed within shored area and tied off to prevent slipping.

Ladders ensure safe entry and exit for workers.

Figure 110

Ladders must

— be placed within the area protected by the shoring or trench box
— be securely tied off at the top
— extend at least 1 metre (3 feet) above shoring
— be inspected regularly for damage
— be placed as close as possible to where personnel are working and never more than 7.5 metres (25 feet) away.

Inspection

Inspection is everyone's responsibility. Whatever the protective system, it should be inspected regularly.

Check timber shoring (Figure 111). Inspect wales for signs of crushing. Crushing indicates structural inadequacy and calls for more struts.

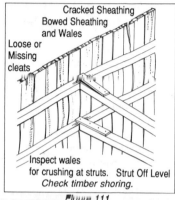

Cracked Sheathing
Bowed Sheathing and Wales
Loose or Missing cleats
Inspect wales for crushing at struts.   Strut Off Level
Check timber shoring.

Figure 111

Check hydraulic shoring (Figure 112) for leaks in hoses and cylinders, bent bases, broken or cracked nipples, and other damaged or defective parts.

Inspect trench boxes (Figure 113) for structural damage, cracks in welds, and other defects. If the box is shifting or settling much more on one side than the other, get out and tell the supervisor.

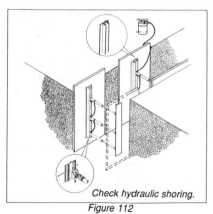

Check hydraulic shoring.

Figure 112

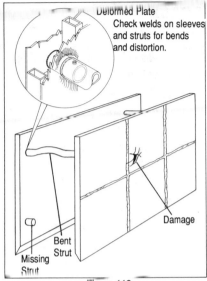

Deformed Plate
Check welds on sleeves and struts for bends and distortion.

Damage

Bent Strut

Missing Strut

Figure 113

Check ground surface for tension cracks which may develop parallel to the trench at a distance one-half to three-quarters of the trench depth. If cracks are detected, alert the crew and check all protective systems carefully.

Check areas adjacent to shoring where water may have entered the trench. A combination of water flow and granular soils can lead to undermining of the trench wall. Such conditions have caused fatalities.

REMEMBER

Never enter a trench more than 1.2 metres (4 feet) deep unless it is sloped, shored, or protected by a trench box.

---

15 CONFINED SPACES

> A confined space is a work area where entry and exit are
> restricted by location, design, or construction and where
> equipment, operations, or atmospheres may pose hazards to
> health and safety.

Typical examples in construction are shafts, basements, sewers,
manholes, mechanical rooms, and storage tanks.

The **physical hazards** of confined spaces include

- poor entry or exit
- cramped work conditions
- extremes of temperature
- operating equipment
- reactive or corrosive residues
- electrical, hydraulic, and pneumatic hazards.

Hazardous **atmospheres** can be

- flammable
- explosive
- toxic
- oxygen-enriched
- oxygen-deficient.

Workers in the carpentry, resilient flooring, and acoustic and interior
systems trades should especially beware of atmospheric hazards created
in confined spaces by the dust from sanding, grinding, and cutting as
well as the vapours from adhesives, solvents, and coatings.

Regulations

The *Regulations for Construction Projects* require that a worker must not
be present in a confined space where there is, or is likely to be,
hazardous gas, vapour, mist, dust, smoke, fume, or oxygen content less
than 18% or more than 23% unless the following measures are taken.

- The confined space must be purged and ventilated to create and
  maintain an atmosphere that will not endanger workers.

- Suitable arrangements must be made to remove a worker from the
  confined space in case of emergency.

- Another worker must be stationed outside the space. If this worker is
  not trained to provide artificial respiration, a person trained to do so
  must be conveniently available.

If the confined space cannot be adequately purged or ventilated, a worker may enter the space only under the following conditions.

- The worker must be equipped with suitable respiratory protection and a full body harness attached to a rope tied to a fixed support outside the space and held by a worker equipped with an alarm (Figure 114).

- There must be a means of communication between the worker inside the space and the worker outside.

- A person trained in artificial respiration and equipped and able to perform rescue operations must be readily available outside the confined space.

WARNING Never try to rescue a worker overcome in a confined space unless you are trained and equipped to do so. Many workers trying to save their buddies have only become victims themselves. Call for emergency help.

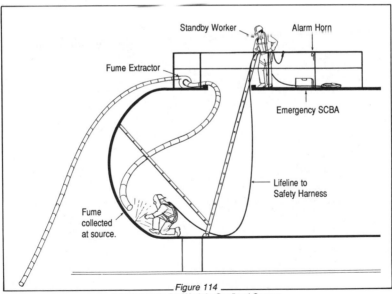

Figure 114
Requirements for Work in Confined Spaces

Air-Testing

Special equipment for testing air quality maybe required to identify or verify suspected atmospheric hazards in a confined space (Figure 115). The testing must be conducted by a competent, trained individual.

If tests indicate a hazardous atmosphere, workers must not enter the space until adequate ventilation and subsequent tests ensure safe air quality.

Ventilation must be continued and air quality monitored as long as workers are in the space.

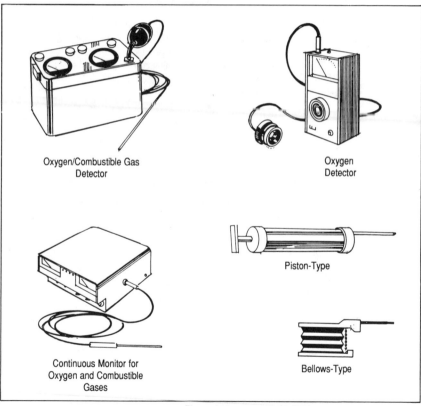

Oxygen/Combustible Gas
Detector

Oxygen
Detector

Piston-Type

Continuous Monitor for
Oxygen and Combustible
Gases

Bellows-Type

Figure 115
Gas Detection Equipment

Labelling

Read and understand the WHMIS supplier labels and other warnings on the products you are required to use on the job.

Follow the supplier's instructions for safe handling and use, particularly with regard to ventilation and any respiratory protection required.

Flammable Products

When using flammable materials in a confined space, take these precautions.

- Provide adequate ventilation, as described above.
- Control sparks and other potential ignition sources.
- Extinguish all pilot lights.
- Have fire extinguishers handy.

Contact cement is one example of a product with fire or explosion potential when used in a small room with poor ventilation, such as a bathroom. Deaths have occurred from explosion and fire when workers finished work and switched off the light in a room where solvent vapours from contact cement or adhesives had accumulated.

Below Grade Hazards

Workers erecting and bracing forms below-grade must often work in areas where movement is restricted (Figure 116). They must be

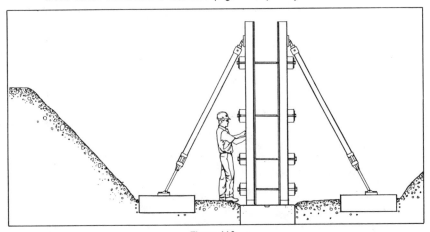

Figure 116

169

constantly aware of hazards underfoot and overhead. The difficulty of the rough terrain and the risk of debris, material, or equipment rolling into the workspace all require special care. Having someone topside to pass down material and keep an eye out for hazards is recommended.

Skylights, Domes, and Ceilings

Drywall workers are sometimes required to work within the confines of newly installed skylights where lighter-than-air gases and fumes may accumulate (Figure 117). Workers should be aware of this hazard. At the first sign of discomfort or disorientation they should leave the area until it has been ventilated.

The air quality in stairwells and close to ceiling lines will often reflect any pollution in the rest of the building or structure. Workers feeling light-headed or experiencing headaches may be inhaling these pollutants. Drowsiness or disorientation can lead to falls. Again, leave the area until it has been ventilated.

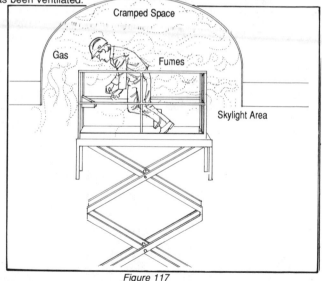

Figure 117

Tunnels and Utility Spaces

These confined spaces may present physical or atmospheric hazards. Many utilities are routed through tunnels or spaces below ground where hazardous atmospheres may collect from containers or operations above or be created by leaks in utilities such as gas and oil.

Shafts

Work to be done in shafts must be carefully planned. Because the work may be of short duration and require only a temporary platform, these jobs are often not given proper attention. But shafts can present various physical and atmospheric hazards against which safeguards must be planned and carried out.

The same requirements that apply to exterior work platforms apply to platforms used inside shafts, tanks, and similar structures, including the regulations regarding suspended access equipment.

Because of the natural draw in shafts, airborne contaminants can be carried through quickly and in large volumes, sometimes with fatal results.

Other Spaces

In addition to the locales already described, beware of apparently harmless areas that can become hazardous because of the products being used there or the work being done (Figure 118). Basements, halls, and small rooms can be dangerous when lack of ventilation and hazardous materials or operations combine to create atmospheric hazards.

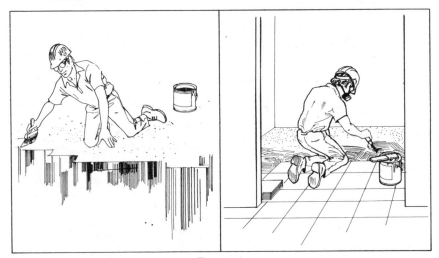

Figure 118

Heating

Heating in confined areas, particularly with propane, involves special hazards and safeguards. Propane is heavier than air and can collect in low-lying areas such as trenches, basements, and shaft bottoms. Propane can also be absorbed into clothing. Workers must therefore use extreme caution in the event of leakage or flame-out.

When propane is burned to fuel heaters and other equipment, it uses up oxygen and releases carbon monoxide and nitrogen oxides. To keep these gases at acceptable levels and to ensure enough oxygen for breathing, adequate ventilation must be provided and maintained.

• Store and secure cylinders upright at all times. Do not store propane indoors or near other fuel storage areas.

• Store cylinders away from buildings, preferably in a separate compound where there is no danger of being struck by falling material or moving equipment. A compound can be constructed from snowfence and T-bars. The barrier provides a means of tying the cylinders upright as well as controlling stock.

• Keep valves fully open to prevent freeze-up.

• Secure cylinders at least 10 feet but no more than 25 feet from the heater (Figure 119).

• Fuel-fired heating devices must not be used in a confined or enclosed space unless there is enough air for combustion and adequate ventilation.

• Protect heaters from damage and overturning.

• Vent exhaust from heaters outside the building or structure.

• Protect fuel supply lines and steam piping for temporary heat from damage.

• Keep a 4A40BC fire extinguisher available wherever propane fuel is being used.

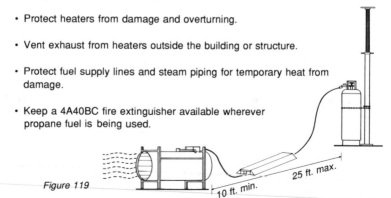

Figure 119

25 ft. max.

10 ft. min.

The requirements for handling, working with, removing, and disposing of asbestos and asbestos-containing products are spelled out in *Asbestos on Construction Projects and in Buildings and Repair Operations* (Ontario Regulation 654/85).

What Is Asbestos?

Asbestos is a naturally occurring material once used widely in the construction industry. Its strength, ability to withstand high temperatures, and resistance to many chemicals made it useful in hundreds of applications. But early widespread use of asbestos has left a potentially dangerous legacy.

> Before any work begins with asbestos, the Ministry of Labour must be notified.

The improper handling of asbestos-containing products may release harmful amounts of fibre. When inhaled, asbestos has been shown to cause the following diseases

— asbestosis
— lung cancer
— mesothelioma (cancer of the lining of the chest and/or abdomen).

Where Can Asbestos Be Found?

Most structures built between 1930 and 1975 will contain products having substantial amounts of asbestos.

If you have any concerns about material that you believe may be asbestos, play it safe and have it checked **before** work is started.

ASBESTOS PRODUCTS IN CONSTRUCTION			
Product	Residential	Commercial/ Institutional	Industrial
Sprayed-On Fireproofing		XX *	
Pipe and Boiler Insulation	X	X	XX
Loose Fill Insulation			X
Asbestos Cement Products	X	X	X
Acoustical Plaster		X	
Acoustical Tile	X	XX	
Vinyl Asbestos	X	X	
Gaskets		X	XX
Roofing Felts		X	X
Asphalt/Asbestos Limpet Spray			X
Drywall Joint-Filling Compound	X	X	
Coatings and Mastics	X	X	X

* Denotes extensive use

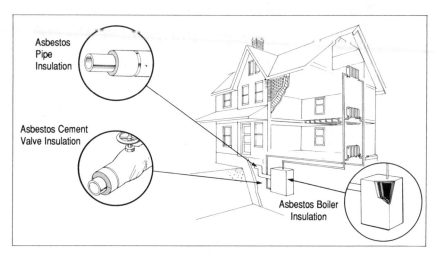

Asbestos Products in Older Residential Buildings

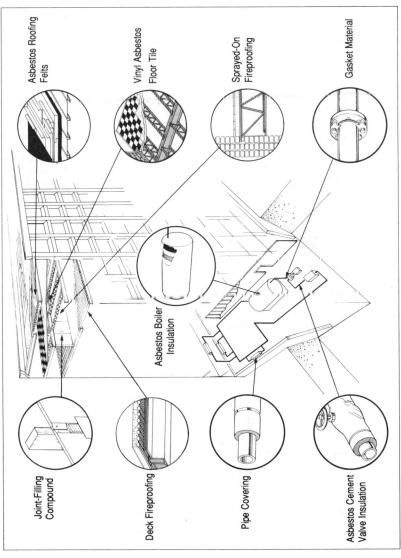

Asbestos Roofing Felts

Vinyl Asbestos Floor Tile

Sprayed-On Fireproofing

Gasket Material

Asbestos Boiler Insulation

Joint-Filling Compound

Deck Fireproofing

Pipe Covering

Asbestos Cement Valve Insulation

Asbestos Products and Locations in Commercial/Institutional Buildings

175

Workers in the carpentry, drywall, resilient flooring, and acoustic and interior systems trades may encounter asbestos in

— light fixtures
— light troughs
— soffits
— transite tile over stairways
— soffits of plazas
— ceiling tile
— 2' x 2' porous tile
— exterior cladding
— insulation
— pre-1975 drywall joint compound
— caulking materials
— gaskets and packings.

Remember, sanding creates fine airborne dust which may stay airborne for 24 hours or longer. Air movements created by heating and air-conditioning systems will spread these airborne particles throughout the building unless the work area is sealed off.

Friable and Non-Friable

Two classes of asbestos products were widely used in the past. The first includes materials easily crumbled or loose in composition. These are referred to as "friable."

The second type includes materials much more durable because they are held together by a binder such as cement, vinyl, or asphalt. These products are termed "non-friable."

Friable material in *Figure 120* was widely used to fireproof steel structures. It can be found on beams, columns, trusses, hoists, and steel pan floors. Sprayed material was also used as a decorative finish and as acoustical insulation on ceilings

The material can be loose, fluffy, and lumpy in texture or, if more gypsum was used, it may be quite hard and durable.

Friable Materials
Sprayed-On Fireproofing

Approved Fireproofing

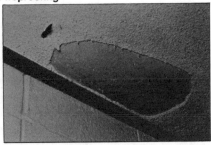

Acoustical Coating

Sprayed Fireproofing

Air-Cell Pipe Insulation

Figure 120

177

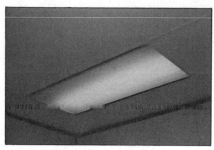

Suspended Ceiling Concealing Fireproofing

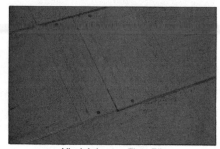

Asbestos-Cement Siding   *Figure 121*   *Vinyl Asbestos Floor Tile*

Encapsulation and Removal

In dealing with asbestos that may be encountered in applications such as fireproofing and cement, the decision whether to encapsulate or remove the material rests with the client/owner.

Many owners of asbestos-containing buildings have decided to reduce the risk of exposure to asbestos. The procedure is normally either removal or encapsulation. Encapsulation means spraying an approved sealant onto or into the material to prevent the release of fibres into the air in the building.

Removal of asbestos is a more permanent solution to the problem. Most removal projects employ the **wet removal** method. Water and a wetting agent are sprayed onto the asbestos. This effectively reduces the quantity of fibres generated when the material is removed.

Spraying Asbestos Ceiling Material with Amended Water Before Wet Removal

Dry removal is normally done only when **wet removal** is impractical – for instance in computer rooms or other areas where there is a chance of water damage to delicate equipment. Dry removal causes excessively high concentrations of asbestos fibres (in excess of 100 fibres per cubic centimetre) and may contaminate other previously "clean" areas.

Dry removal projects should include extensive filtered exhaust systems to create a slight negative pressure in the work area. This will reduce the chance of spreading asbestos fibres.

Another solution is to enclose the asbestos with a physical barrier such as drywall. This is normally done where the area is not going to be entered frequently or altered later.

Precautions to prevent the spread of asbestos fibres during installation of the enclosure should be the same as those taken for encapsulation and removal.

Types

Five factors determine whether, under Ontario law, an asbestos operation is Type 1, Type 2, or Type 3. The factors are

— nature of asbestos material
— nature of work activity
— applicability of alternate controls
— duration of exposure
— risk to bystanders.

These five factors can be used to categorize the proposed operation into one of three types.

Type 1 —   generally presents little hazard to workers or bystanders (for example, installing vinyl asbestos floor tile).

Type 2 —   may create exposure exceeding acceptable limits but work is of short duration (for example, removing six square inches of asbestos fireproofing to attach a new pipe hanger).

Type 3 —   major exposures, exceeding acceptable limits, involving frequent or prolonged exposure, and posing serious risks to both workers and to bystanders (for example, full-scale removal of asbestos fireproofing in an occupied building).

Respirators for Different Types of Asbestos Operations

 **Half-Face Mask**	For Type 1 or Type 2 operations For Type 3 wet removal of chrysotile
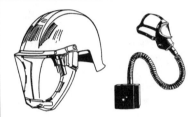 Powered Air-Purifying Respirators	For Type 3 wet removal of amosite or crocidolite or power cutting asbestos cement products
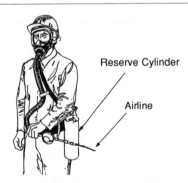 Reserve Cylinder Airline Combination Airline/SCBA (Self-Contained Breathing Apparatus) Unit	For Type 3 dry removal of asbestos (any species)

Type 1 Operations

Installing or removing manufactured products containing asbestos (for example, vinyl asbestos tile, acoustic tile, gaskets, seals, packings, brake pads and linings, clutch facings, and asbestos cement products).

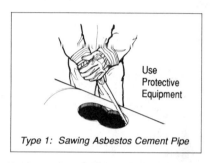

Use Protective Equipment

Type 1: Sawing Asbestos Cement Pipe

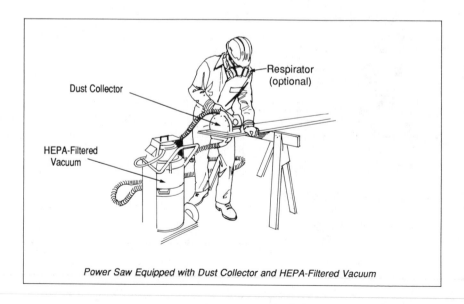

Respirator (optional)

Dust Collector

HEPA-Filtered Vacuum

Power Saw Equipped with Dust Collector and HEPA-Filtered Vacuum

Type 2 Operations

Removing all or part of a false ceiling in buildings which contain sprayed asbestos fireproofing where there is a strong likelihood of asbestos dust resting on top of the ceiling because the fireproofing is damaged or deteriorating.

Eating, smoking, chewing, or drinking is not permitted in the work areas.

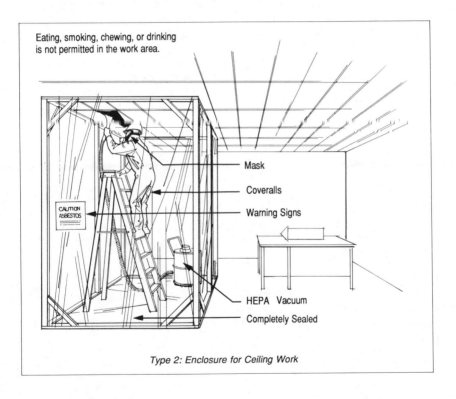

Type 2: Enclosure for Ceiling Work

Type 3 Operations

The following operations involve serious potential exposure to asbestos dust and accordingly are subject to the most stringent precautions:

— removing or encapsulating asbestos insulation or fireproofing (other than minor Type 2 operations)

— cleaning or removing air-handling equipment in buildings with sprayed asbestos fireproofing

— repairs, alterations, or demolition of kilns, metallurgical furnaces, and other installations where asbestos refractory materials are present

— repair, alteration, or demolition of buildings which are or were used to manufacture asbestos products

— cutting, grinding, or abrading asbestos products with power tools not equipped with dust collectors and HEPA filtered vacuums.

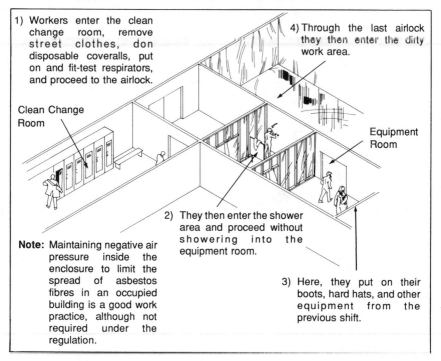

1) Workers enter the clean change room, remove street clothes, don disposable coveralls, put on and fit-test respirators, and proceed to the airlock.

Clean Change Room

4) Through the last airlock they then enter the dirty work area.

Equipment Room

2) They then enter the shower area and proceed without showering into the equipment room.

Note: Maintaining negative air pressure inside the enclosure to limit the spread of asbestos fibres in an occupied building is a good work practice, although not required under the regulation.

3) Here, they put on their boots, hard hats, and other equipment from the previous shift.

Typical Entry/Decontamination Layout

184

Asbestos Waste Management

The off-site handling and disposal of asbestos waste is governed by the *Environmental Protection Act*. Regulations regarding the transportation of dangerous goods under either the federal Department of Transport or the Ontario Ministry of Transportation may also apply.

Some municipalities may not accept asbestos waste at landfill operations. Contractors are urged to check with local authorities for the nearest disposal site and with the district office of the Ministry of the Environment.

Other Methods

Contractors who wish to use methods and equipment other than those described in this chapter must submit their proposals in writing to the Ministry of Labour for review and written approval **before the work begins.**

Plastic Shovel

Warning Label

Worker Placing Asbestos Waste in Container
Note plastic bag inside drum.

17 WATER AND ICE

Construction over and around water and ice presents special dangers. Precautions specifically developed for such construction must be taken before work begins.

This chapter outlines general safeguards that must be followed whenever personnel are required to work over water or on ice, including construction on bridges, wharves, dams, locks, and breakwaters.

Guardrails

The requirements for guardrails specified in Chapter 8 of this manual apply to work stations over water or ice.

Ramps

Ramps must be
— at least 48 centimetres (18 inches) wide
— not sloped more than 1 in 3 (20 degrees) and
— where slope exceeds 1 in 8 (6 degrees), have cleats 19 x 38 millimetres (1 inch by 2 inches) secured at regular intervals not more than 50 centimetres (20 inches) apart.

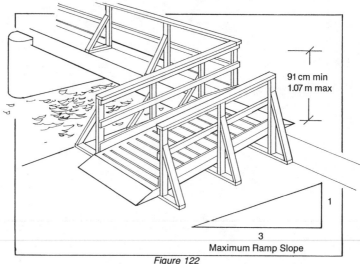

91 cm min
1.07 m max

1

3
Maximum Ramp Slope

Figure 122
186

When a ramp is used for equipment such as wheelbarrows and a worker may fall from the ramp a distance of 1.2 metres (4 feet) or more, the ramp must be provided with guardrails (Figure 122).

Floating Work Platforms

When used on a construction project, rafts, scows, and similar vessels are considered work platforms. As such, they are subject to certain requirements.

- Guardrails must be provided along open edges. The guardrails may be removed at the working side of the platform, provided workers are protected by alternate measures such as using safety belts or being attached to rescue ropes.
- Workers on floating platforms must wear lifejackets. A lifejacket provides enough buoyancy to keep the wearer's head above water, face up, without effort.
- Appropriate rescue measures must be provided.

In addition, the positioning and securing of vessels used as work platforms should be supervised and undertaken by experienced personnel.

Fall-Arrest Systems

The requirements specified in Chapter 6 of this manual apply to work over water or ice.

Safety Nets

Safety nets may be necessary when structural design, loading access, worker mobility, or other factors make guardrails and fall-arrest systems impractical (Figure 123).

Safety nets must be installed
— in accordance with manufacturer's instructions
— as close under the working level as practical but no lower than 9 metres (30 feet)
— with enough clearance to prevent contact with any surface below if a worker falls into the net
— with an outward extension of 3 metres (10 feet) from the outermost projection of the structure.

Take the following precautions.

- Perimeter wire rope must be at least 13 millimetres (1/2 inch) in diameter and be supported at a maximum spacing of every 15 metres (50 feet).
- Nets must be secured along their entire length at intervals not exceeding 1 metre (3 feet).
- When nets are laced or joined together, they must be attached at intervals not exceeding 15 centimetres (6 inches).
- Because of daily exposure to all kinds of weather, nets should be made of polypropylene rope with ultraviolet (UV) retardant.

Figure 123

Lifejackets and PFDs

Lifejackets must be worn by workers exposed to the danger of drowning in water deep enough for the lifejacket to be effective.

A PFD is a personal flotation device.

For boating to and from the worksite, boats must be equipped with one approved lifejacket for each person on board.

"Approved" refers to approval by Transport Canada (look for the Transport Canada label).

A lifejacket is a flotation device that provides buoyancy adequate to keep the wearer's head above water, face up, without effort by the wearer.

Lifejackets and PFDs differ in one important feature: a lifejacket will keep an unconscious person's face out of the water whereas a PFD does not provide this protection.

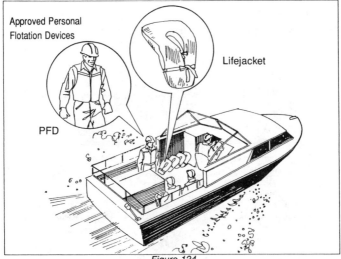

Figure 124

Rescue

Where personnel are exposed to the risk of drowning, two or more workers must be available for a rescue operation. A boat must also be available and furnished with the following rescue equipment (minimum):

— a ring buoy attached to 15 metres (50 feet) of polypropylene rope 9.5 millimetres (3/8 inch) in diameter
— a boat hook and
— lifejackets for each person in the rescue crew.

Where a manually-operated boat is not suitable or where the water is likely to be rough or swift, the rescue boat must be power-driven. The engine should be started and checked daily.

Rescue equipment such as boats must be stored on or near the project, ready for use.

Where there is a current in the water, a single length of line must be extended across the water downstream from all work locations and be fitted with buoys or similar objects to keep a person afloat. The line must be securely fastened at each end to adequate anchorage.

An alarm system must be installed and maintained to alert workers to the need for an emergency rescue.

All of these requirements are illustrated in Figure 125.

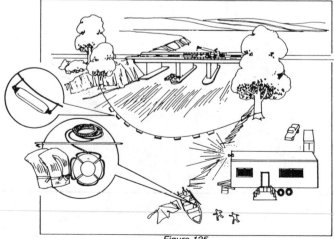

Figure 125

Transporting Workers by Boat

When navigating any Canadian waterway, boats and other floating vessels must comply with the requirements of the Canada Shipping Act. Refer specifically to the Small Vessel Regulations and Collision Regulations under the Act.

Generally, boats used for construction operations are not longer than 5.5 metres (18 feet). Boats in this class must be equipped with at least
— one approved lifejacket for each person on board
— two oarlocks or two paddles
— one bailer or one manual pump
— one Class B1 fire extinguisher
— one sound signalling device.

These items are shown in Figure 126.

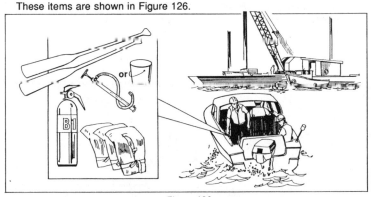

Figure 126

All power boats require some navigation lights. For appropriate regulations, consult the *Safe Boating Guide* published by the Canadian Coast Guard.

As a rough guide only, Transport Canada has issued the following passenger capacity for boats:

Length of Boat	Number of Persons	Maximum Weight Load
3 metres (10')	2	185 kg (410 lbs)
3.7 metres (12')	3	260 kg (572 lbs)
4 metres (14')	4	335 kg (737 lbs)
5 metres (16')	5	440 kg (968 lbs)

In rough water conditions, it is advisable to reduce passenger capacity by one as a further safety precaution.

Ice Testing

Work, travel, and parking on frozen bodies of water should be avoided whenever possible and be done only as a last resort. The ice **must** be tested before any workers or vehicles are allowed onto the surface. Loads that may safely travel on ice may not necessarily be left on ice for extended periods of time. This applies especially to parked vehicles.

Before testing, learn as much as possible about ice conditions from local residents. Testing requires at least two persons on foot proceeding with caution. Each person must wear an approved lifejacket or, preferably, an approved flotation suit.

For ice testing, a flotation suit or lifejacket is required because a person falling into frigid water may lose consciousness and the suit or lifejacket will keep the person's face out of the water.

Members of the ice-testing crew should stay at about 10 metres (30 feet) apart. The lead member must wear a safety harness attached to a polypropylene rescue rope 9.5 millimetres (3/8 inch) thick, at least 20 metres (65 feet) long, and held by the trailing crew member (Figure 127).

Figure 127

Clear blue ice is the most desirable for strength. White or opaque ice forms from wet snow and has a higher air content. It is less dense and therefore weaker than clear blue ice. Grey ice indicates the presence of water from thawing and should not be trusted as a load-bearing surface.

The lead crew member should cut test holes every 8 metres (25 feet) or so. If ice is less than 10 centimetres (4 inches) thick, the lead and trailing crew members should vacate the area immediately.

The biggest uncertainty about the load-bearing capacity of ice is the natural variation in thickness and quality that can occur over a given area. Currents and springs can cause variations in thickness without changing the overall surface appearance of the ice. Considerable variation in ice thickness can occur where rivers have significant currents or where high banks may create springs. Similar situations occur in lakes at the inlet and outlet of rivers.

Only the thickness of continuously frozen ice should be used to determine bearing capacity. The basis for capacity should be the **minimum** thickness measured.

In addition to testing for thickness, crews should check ice for cracking. Except during thaw periods, cracks do not necessarily indicate a reduction in bearing capacity.

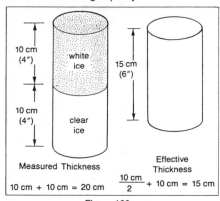

Figure 128

Ice thickness is determined by the full thickness of clear blue ice plus half the thickness of any white, continuously frozen ice (Figure 128).

For repeated work or travel over ice, the surface must be tested regularly to ensure continued safety. Ice must also be tested regularly near currents or eddies and around permanent structures like abutments.

Bearing Capacity of Ice

Where heavy equipment such as cranes or structures such as concrete forms are to be placed on ice for extended periods, ask an experienced consultant for advice on bearing capacity, load methods, and inspection procedures. With professional advice it is possible to increase bearing capacity considerably. But careful control is required over surface operations, loading procedures, and ice monitoring.

In other cases, refer to Graph 1 for allowable **moving** loads on various thicknesses of clear blue ice. Remember – the graph is **not** to be used for loads parked, stored, or otherwise left stationary for long periods of time.

Certain types of cracking can affect the bearing capacity of ice. For a single dry crack wider than 2.5 centimetres (1 inch), reduce loads by one third; for intersecting cracks of this size, reduce loads by two thirds. Dry cracks can be repaired by filling in with water or slush.

A wet crack indicates penetration through the ice to water below. Bearing capacity can be dangerously lowered. For a single wet crack, reduce loads by half. For two wet cracks meeting at right angles, reduce loads by three quarters. Most wet cracks refreeze as strong as the original ice. A core sample should be taken to determine the depth of healing.

Other Considerations

- Ice roads must be at least 40 centimetres (16 inches) thick along their entire length.
- Ice roads should not be built up more than 10 centimetres (4 inches) in one day and must not be used or reflooded until the top layer has completely frozen.
- While an ice road is in use it must be checked daily for thickness, cracks, thawing, and other conditions.
- All rescue equipment listed earlier in this chapter must be readily available.
- A life ring attached to 20 metres (65 feet) of polypropylene rescue rope 9.5 millimetres (3/8 inch) thick must be kept within 35 metres (115 feet) of the work area.
- A warm place such as a truck cab or hut must be provided and made known to personnel near the worksite.

Recommended Bearing Capacity
Based on Experience - Moving Loads Only

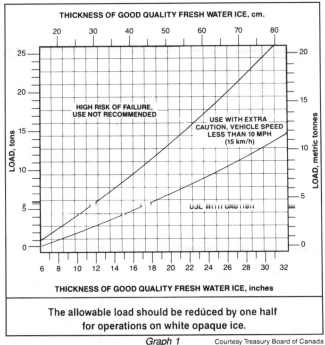

Graph 1   Courtesy Treasury Board of Canada

MAXIMUM SPEEDS FOR TRUCKS AND SIMILAR EQUIPMENT
TRAVELLING ON ICE

Depth of Water		Maximum Speed	
metres	feet	km/h	mph
0.3	1	3	2
0.6	2	5	3
1.2	4	8	5
2.5	8	10	6
5.0	16	15	10
over	over	20	12

MINIMUM ICE THICKNESSES FOR FOOT AND VEHICLE TRAVEL

Minimum 10 cm (4")

3 m (10')   3 m (10')

Minimum 18 cm (7")

Minimum 33 cm (13")

Trade Specifics

18 CARPENTRY HAND TOOLS

Injuries with hand tools are not often serious but they do involve lost time. Common causes include using the wrong tool, using the right tool improperly, haste, and lack of training or experience.

Hand Saws

Select the right saw for the job.

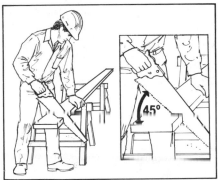

The approved method of crosscutting.

A 9 point is not meant for crosscutting hardwood. It can jump up and severely cut the worker's hand or thumb.

For this kind of work the right choice is an 11 point (+). When starting a cut, keep your thumb up high to guide the saw and avoid injury.

The side and tooth-edge views of a typical crosscut saw. This saw is used for cutting across the grain and has a different cutting action than that of the ripsaw. The crosscut saw cuts on both the forward and backward strokes.

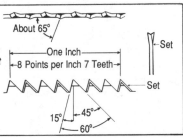

About 65°
One Inch
8 Points per Inch 7 Teeth
Set
Set
15° 45°
60°

For cutting softwood, select a 9 point
(-). The teeth will remove sawdust
easily and keep the saw from binding
and bucking.

Ripping requires a ripsaw. Check the
illustrations for the differences in teeth
and action between rip and crosscut
saws.

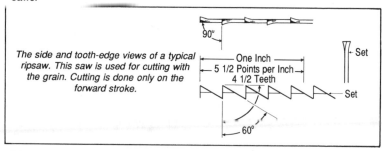

The side and tooth-edge views of a typical ripsaw. This saw is used for cutting with the grain. Cutting is done only on the forward stroke.

90°

One Inch

5 1/2 Points per Inch
4 1/2 Teeth

Set

Set

60°

Wood Chisels

Most injuries with this tool can be
prevented by keeping the hand that
holds the work **behind**, not in front of,
the chisel.

A dull or incorrectly sharpened chisel is
difficult to control and tedious to work
with.

Chisels not in use or stored in a toolbox
should have protective caps.

Wood chisels are tempered to be very
hard. The metal is brittle and will
shatter easily against hard surfaces.

Never use a chisel for prying.

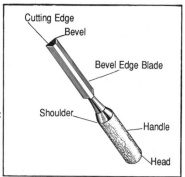

Cutting Edge

Bevel

Bevel Edge Blade

Shoulder

Handle

Head

With chisels and other struck tools, **always wear eye protection**. Gloves are recommended to help prevent cuts and bruises.

Cold Chisels

Cold chisels are used to cut or shape soft metals as well as concrete and brick.

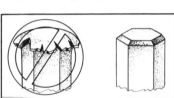

Flat

Cape

In time the struck end will mushroom. This should be ground off. Don't use chisels with mushroomed heads. Fragments can fly off and cause injury.

Mushroom   Dressed Head

Axes and Hatchets

In construction, axes are mainly used for making stakes or wedges and splitting or shaping rough timbers.

Unless it has a striking face, don't use the hatchet as a hammer. The head or the wooden handle can crack and break.

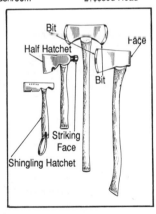

Bit

Face

Half Hatchet

Bit

Striking Face

Shingling Hatchet

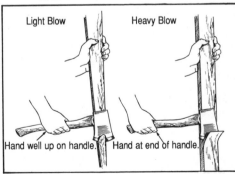

Light Blow   Heavy Blow

Hand well up on handle.   Hand at end of handle.

Grasp the handle of the hand axe approximately halfway between the ends to strike a light blow and at the end of the handle to obtain the necessary swing for a heavy blow.

Hatchets with striking faces are meant only for driving common nails, not for striking chisels, punches, drills, or other hardened metal tools.

Never use an axe or hatchet as a wedge or chisel and strike it with a hammer.

Most carpenters prefer a hatchet with a solid or tubular steel handle and a hammer head with a slot for pulling nails.

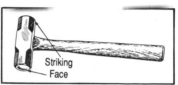

Striking Face

Sledgehammers

Sledgehammers are useful for drifting heavy timbers and installing and dismantling formwork. They can knock heavy panels into place and drive stakes in the ground for bracing.

Sledgehammers can also be used to drive thick tongue-and-groove planking tightly together. Use a block of scrap wood to prevent damage to the planks.

The main hazard is the weight of the head. Once the hammer is in motion it's almost impossible to stop the swing. Serious bruises and broken bones have been caused by sledgehammers off-target and out of control.

Missing the target with the head and hitting the handle instead can weaken the stem. Another swing can send the head flying.

Always check handle and head. Make sure head is secure and tight. Replace damaged handles.

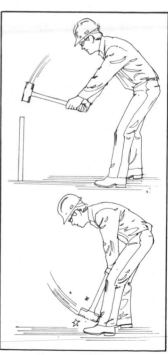

Hammer Off-Target

As with any striking or struck tool, always wear eye protection.

Swinging a sledgehammer is hard work. Avoid working to the point of fatigue. Make sure you have the strength to maintain aim and control.

Claw Hammers

These are available in many shapes, weights, and sizes for various purposes. Handles can be wood or steel (solid or tubular). Metal handles are usually covered with shock-absorbing material.

Start with a good quality hammer of medium weight (16 ounces) with a grip suited to the size of your hand.

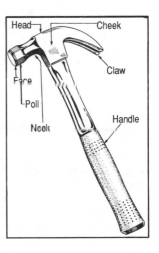

Rest your arm occasionally to avoid tendinitis. Avoid overexertion in pulling out nails. Use a crow bar or nail puller when necessary.

When nailing, start with one "soft" hit, that is, with fingers holding the nail. Then let go and drive the nail in the rest of the way.

Strike with the hammer face at right angles to the nailhead. Glancing blows can lead to flying nails. Clean the face on sandpaper to remove glue and gum.

Don't use nail hammers on concrete, steel chisels, hardened steel-cut nails, or masonry nails.

Discard any hammer with a dented, chipped, or mushroomed striking face or with claws broken, deformed, or nicked inside the nail slot.

Utility Knives

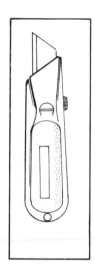

Utility knives cause more cuts than any other sharp-edged cutting tool in construction.

Use knives with retractable blades only.

Always cut away from your body, especially away from your free hand. When you're done with the knife, retract the blade at once. A blade left exposed is dangerous, particularly in a toolbox.

Screwdrivers

More than any other tool, the screwdriver is used for jobs it was never meant to do.

Screwdrivers are not intended for prying, scraping, chiselling, scoring, or punching holes.

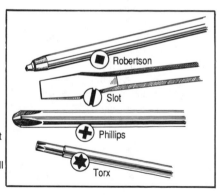

The most common abuse of the screwdriver is using one that doesn't fit or match the fastener. That means using a screwdriver too big or too small for the screw or not matched to the screw head.

The results are cuts and punctures from slipping screwdrivers, eye injuries from flying fragments of pried or struck screwdrivers, and damaged work.

Always make a pilot hole before driving a screw.

Start with one or two "soft" turns, that is, with the fingers of your free hand on the screw. Engage one or two threads, make sure the screw is going in straight, then take your fingers away.

You can put your fingers on the shank to help guide and hold the screwdriver. But the main action is on the handle, which should be large enough to allow enough grip and torque to drive the screw.

Note: All cross point screws are not designed to be driven by a Phillips screwdriver. Phillips screws and drivers are only one type among several cross-point systems. They are *not* interchangeable.

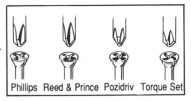

Phillips   Reed & Prince   Pozidriv   Torque Set

Hand Planes

Hazards include the risk of crush and scrape injuries when the hand holding the plane strikes the work or objects nearby. Cuts and sliver injuries are also common.

The hand plane requires some strength and elbow grease to use properly. The hazards of overexertion and tendinitis can be aggravated by using a dull iron or too short a plane.

Use the plane suited to the job and keep the iron sharp.

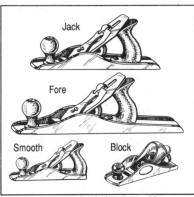

Various types of planes used by woodworkers.

For long surfaces like door edges, use a fore plane 18" long and 2 3/8" wide or a jointer plane 24" long and 2 5/8" wide.

For shorter surfaces, use a jack plane 15" long and 2 3/8" wide or a smoothing plane 10" long and 2 3/8" wide.

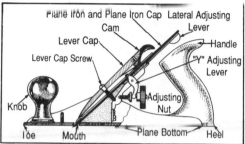

A typical smoothing plane and its parts.

Remember that sharp tools require less effort and reduce the risk of fatigue, overexertion, and back strain.

Work can also be easier with a door jack and supports on your work bench.

Plumb Bobs

The weight of a mercury-filled plumb bob will surprise you. Designed for use in windy conditions, the bob has considerable weight in proportion to its surface area.

The weight and point of the bob can make it dangerous. Ensure that all is clear below when you lower the bob.

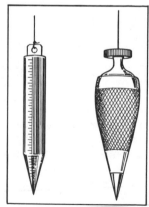

The solid plumb bob.

Don't let it fall out of your pocket,
apron, or tool bag. The same goes for
the standard solid bob.

Crow Bars

Any steel bar 25-150 cm long and
sharpened at one end is often called a
crow bar.

The tools include pry bars, pinch bars,
and wrecking bars. Shorter ones
usually have a curved claw for pulling
nails and a sharp, angled end for
prying.

Nail Pulling

Pulling out nails can be easier with a
crow bar than a claw hammer.

In some cases, a nail-puller does the
job best. Keep the hand holding the
claw well away from the striking handle.

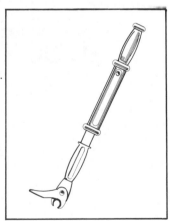

Lifting

Loads levered, lifted, or shifted by bars
can land on fingers and toes.

- Make sure to clear the area and
  maintain control of the load.
- Have enough rollers and blocking
  ready.
- Never —not even for a split second
  — put fingers or toes under the
  load.

Nail-Puller

General

Try to avoid prying, pulling, wedging, or
lifting at sharp angles or overhead.

Wherever possible, keep the bar at
right angles to the work.

Wear eye protection and, where
necessary,face protection.

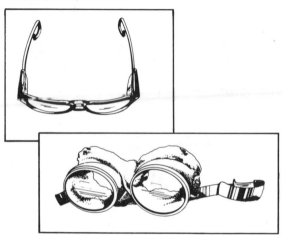

19 DRYWALL HAND TOOLS

The main hazards in the trade are
- back, spine, and shoulder injuries from handling and installing drywall
- falls from ladders, benches, and scaffolds.

To help prevent injuries from overexertion, refer to Chapter 4 BACK CARE. For the safe use of access equipment, refer to Chapters 7-11.

The following chapter concentrates on hand tools commonly used in the trade.

Wallboard Saws

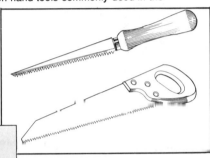

Store with teeth down at all times.

Use caution when moving around or climbing up and down with saws.

Take care when cutting blind into wall or ceiling spaces.
Check for concealed pipes and wiring.

Knives

Knives with retractable blades are recommended over those with fixed blades.

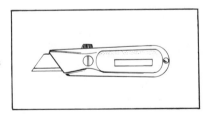

Cut carefully when your free hand is supporting the wallboard, especially from behind.

When the cut is finished, retract the blade or protect it with a sheath or scabbard.

Lath Hammers

Check head for looseness and handle for splits or cracks.

Strike with the hammer at right angles to the nailhead. This will avoid the glancing blows that can send nails flying. It will also prevent dents and other damage to the board.

Lines

Eye injuries have been caused by the sudden release of level and plumb lines under tension.

Make sure that lines are secure. That includes the nails or other fasteners used to hold them in place.

Wallboard Lifter

This device helps to prevent back strain, jammed fingers, and damaged sheets.

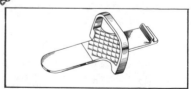

Spirit Level

Harmless in itself, the level can be dangerous when dropped from heights. Handle with care.

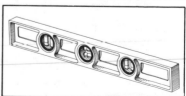

Tin Snips

Snips are available in right, left, and straight cut models.

Wear eye and hand protection when cutting with tin snips.

Don't use snips to cut heavy wire. You can nick and ruin the cutting edge.

Keep cutting head pointed down and jaws closed when snips are in tool pouch or not in use.

Sheetmetal edges can be razor-sharp. Wear gloves.

Triangular pieces tend to flip up when cut. Wear eye protection.

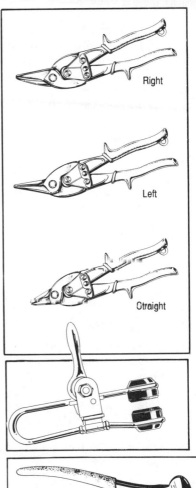

Line Clips

Used for holding metal studs, rubber-tipped line clips help prevent finger and hand injuries. Don't apply too much tension. Clips may spring open and slip down or fall off, leaving you with no control of material.

End Nippers

These are used for cutting suspended ceiling drop wires.

Wear eye protection against flying bits of wire. The teeth on nippers have also been known to break off and injure eyes.

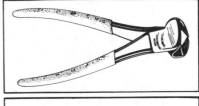

Magnetic Punch

Wire Benders

Use both hands to operate wire benders. Solid footing and balance are also essential.

Stud Crimper

Beware of pinch points at jaws and between handles.

Stud Cutter

Wear eye protection. Beware of pinch points and sharp edges.

Whitney Punch

Use two hands with the punch. Solid footing and balance are essential. Beware of pinch points between handles.

Suspenders

Suspenders are recommended to help support the weight of tools and tool pouch.

Suspenders give hips a break by transferring the entire weight to the shoulders, which can better support it.

Finishing Knives and Trowels

Taping knives, broad knives, finishing knives, putty knives, and joint trowels all have one thing in common — they become exceedingly sharp with use.

Beware of sharp edges when using and storing the tools. Take particular care not to drop knives and trowels from work platforms. They can seriously injure workers below.

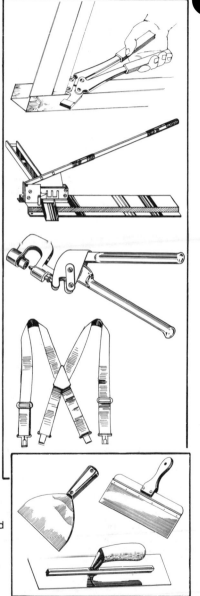

Beware of sharp edges when using and storing the tools. Take particular care not to drop knives and trowels from work platforms. They can seriously injure workers below.

WARNING

Any type of leg extension is expressly forbidden by the *Regulations for Construction Projects*.

Stilts and similar devices are against the law.

If found in violation of the regulation, you will be fined by the Ministry of Labour and your stilts may be confiscated.

20 POWER TOOLS - DRILLS, PLANES, ROUTERS

Safety Basics

- Make sure that electric tools are properly grounded or double-insulated.
- Never remove or tamper with safety devices.
- Study the manufacturer's instructions before operating any new or unfamiliar electric tool.
- Always use a ground fault circuit interrupter (GFCI) with any portable electric tool operated outdoors or in wet locations.
- Before making adjustments or changing attachments, always disconnect the tool from the power source.
- When operating electric tools, **always** wear eye protection.
- When operating tools in confined spaces or for prolonged periods, wear hearing protection.
- Make sure that the tool is held firmly and the material properly secured before turning on the tool.

Drills

Types

With suitable attachments, the drill can be used for disc sanding, sawing holes, driving screws, and grinding. However, when such applications are repeatedly or continuously required, tools specifically designed for the work should be used.

Trim carpenters will generally select a 1/4- or 3/8-inch trigger-controlled variable speed drill (Figure 129). Simply by increasing pressure on the trigger, the operator can change drill speed from 0 to 2,000 rpm.

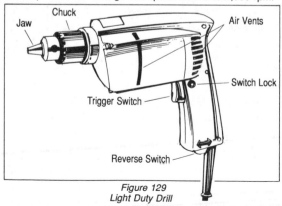

Figure 129
Light Duty Drill

Carpenters working in heavy structural construction such as bridges, trusses, and waterfront piers will usually select the slower but more powerful one or two-speed reversible 1/2- or 3/4-inch drill (Figure 130a).

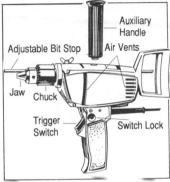

Auxiliary Handle

Adjustable Bit Stop Air Vents

Jaw Chuck

Trigger Switch Switch Lock

Figure 130a
Heavy-Duty Drill

Size of the drill is determined by the maximum opening of the chuck. For instance, a 3/8-inch drill will take only bits or attachments with a shank up to 3/8-inch wide.

For drywall screws, a drywall screw gun (130b) should be used. The driving bit should be replaced when worn. Select a gun that can hang from your tool belt so it does not have to be continuously hand-held.

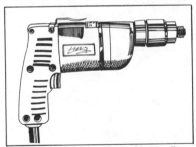

Attachments

Figure 130b
Drywall Screw Gun

Attachments such as speed-reducing screwdrivers, disc sanders, and buffers (Figure 131) can help prevent fatigue and undue muscle strain. A right-angle drive attachment (Figure 132) is very useful in tight corners and other hard-to-reach places.

Cutting and drilling attachments must be kept sharp to avoid overloading the motor. Operators should not crowd or push the tool beyond capacity. Such handling can burn out the motor, ruin the material, and injure the operator in the event of a kickback.

Some attachments, such as hole saws, spade bits, and screwdrivers (Figure 133) require considerable control by the operator. If the operator does not feed the attachment slowly and carefully into the material, the drill can suddenly stop and severely twist or break the operator's arm. Stock should be clamped or otherwise secured to prevent it from moving. This will also enable the operator to control the tool with both hands and absorb sudden twists or stops caused by obstructions such as knots or hidden nails.

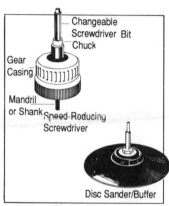

Figure 131
Drill Attachments

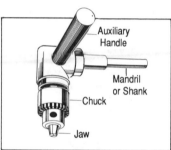

Figure 132
Right-Angle Drive
Attachment

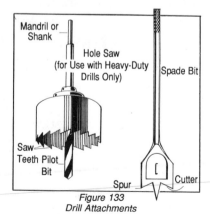

Figure 133
Drill Attachments

Operators must restrain the drill just before the bit or cutting attachment emerges through the material, especially when oversized spade bits are used. Sides of the bit often become hooked on the ragged edge of the nearly completed hole and make the drill come to a sudden stop that can wrench the operator's arm.

At the first sign of the bit breaking through the material, the operator should withdraw the drill and complete the work from the other side. This will produce a cleaner job and prevent the material from cracking or splintering.

The same result can be obtained by clamping a back-up piece to the material and drilling into that.

Select the bit or attachment suitable to the size of the drill and the work to be done. To operate safely and efficiently, the shanks of bits and attachments must turn true.

Make sure that the bit or attachment is properly seated and tightened in the chuck.

Some operations require the use of an impact or hammer drill. For instance, drilling large holes in concrete or rock with a carboloy bit should be done with an impact drill (Figure 134).

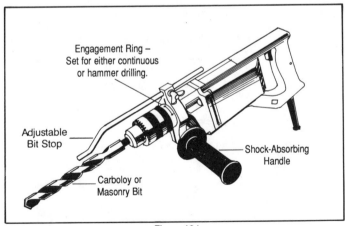

Figure 134
Impact or Hammer Drill

Follow manufacturers' instructions when selecting and using a bit or attachment, especially with drills or work unfamiliar to you.

Working with Small Pieces

Drilling into small pieces of material may look harmless, but if the pieces are not clamped down and supported, they can spin with the bit before the hole is completed.

If a small piece starts to twist or spin with the drill, the operator can be injured. Small work pieces should be properly secured and supported. Never try to drill with one hand and hold a small piece of material with the other.

Drilling from Ladders

Standing on a ladder to drill holes in walls and ceilings (Figure 135) can be hazardous. The top and bottom of the ladder must be secured to prevent the ladder from slipping or sliding when the operator puts pressure on the drill.

When drilling from a ladder, never reach out to either side. Overreaching can cause the ladder to slide or tip.

Never stand on the top step or paint shelf of a stepladder. Stand at least two steps down from the top. When working from an extension ladder, stand no higher than the fourth rung from the top.

When drilling from a ladder, never support yourself by holding onto a pipe or any other grounded object. Electric current can travel from the hand holding the drill through your heart to the hand holding the pipe.

A minor shock can make you lose your balance. A major shock can badly burn or even kill you.

Operation

Always plug in the drill with the switch **OFF**.

Before starting to drill, turn on the tool for a moment to make sure that the shank of the bit or attachment is centred and running true.

Punch a layout hole or drill a pilot hole in the material so that the bit won't slip or slide when you start drilling. A pilot hole is particularly important for drilling into hard material such as concrete or metal.

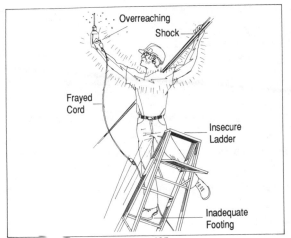

Figure 135
Drilling and Ladder Hazards

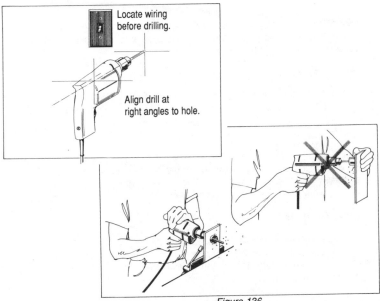

Figure 136
Right and Wrong Ways of Drilling Small Pieces

With the drill **OFF**, put the point of the bit in the pilot hole or punched layout hole.

Hold the drill firmly in one hand or, if necessary, in both hands at the correct drilling angle (Figure 136).

Turn on the switch and feed the drill into the material with the pressure and control required by the size of the drill and the type of material.

Don't try to enlarge a hole by reaming it out with the sides of the bit. Switch to a larger bit.

While drilling deep holes, especially with a twist bit, withdraw the drill several times with the motor running to clear the cuttings.

Never support material on your knee while drilling. Material should be firmly supported on a bench or other work surface for drilling.

Remove the bit from the drill as soon as you have finished that phase of your work.

When drilling into floors, ceilings, and walls, beware of plumbing and especially of wiring.

Remember that the longer you work, the heavier the drill feels, particularly when working overhead. Take a breather now and then to relax your arms and shoulders.

Drilling Timbers

When drilling timbers with a self-feeding auger bit (Figure 137), do not underestimate the physical pressure required to maintain control of the tool. Such work calls for a heavy-duty, low-rpm drill, 1/2 or 3/4 inch in size.

Never attempt to drill heavy timbers by yourself, especially when working on a scaffold or other work platform. If the self-feeding auger bit digs into a hidden knot or other obstruction, the sudden torque can twist or wrench your arm and throw you off balance.

Other Materials

The main hazard in drilling materials other than wood is leaning too heavily on the tool. This can not only overload and burn out the motor but also cause injury if you are thrown off balance by the drill suddenly twisting or stopping.

Always use a drill powerful enough for the job and a bit or attachment suited to the size of the drill and the nature of the work. As at other times, punching a layout hole or drilling a pilot hole can make the job safer and more efficient.

The drill press stand (Figure 138) is ideal for drilling holes in metal accurately and safely. Small pieces can be clamped in a vise and bolted to the table. This prevents the workpiece from spinning when the drill penetrates the metal.

The drill press can also be used for cutting large holes in wood with a hole saw or speed bit. The stability of the press and the operator's control over cutting speed eliminate sudden torque.

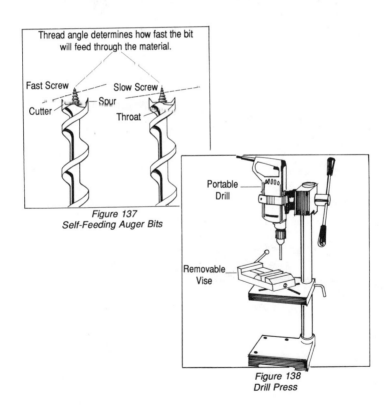

Thread angle determines how fast the bit will feed through the material.

Fast Screw   Slow Screw

Cutter   Spur   Throat

Figure 137
Self-Feeding Auger Bits

Portable Drill

Removable Vise

Figure 138
Drill Press

Planes

Available in various types and sizes, electric planes are generally
operated in similar ways. Adjustments between models may differ,
however, depending on specific features.

Planes may be equipped with

— outfeed tables (back shoes) that are either fixed or movable
— infeed tables (front shoes) that move straight up and down or move
  up and down on angle to keep the gap between cutter head and
  table as small as possible
— cutter heads with two or more straight blades (also called *knives* or
  cutter blades)
— cutter heads with two curved blades.

Follow the safety basics that apply to other electric tools. As with any
powered tool, never operate an electric plane while wearing a scarf, open
jacket, or other loose clothing. Always wear eye protection.

Standard Plane

• Hold with both hands to avoid contact with cutter blades.

• Always keep both hands on the plane until motor stops.

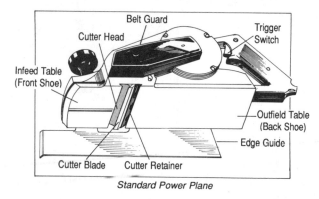

Standard Power Plane

- Use the edge guide to direct the plane along the desired cut. Never try to guide the plane with your fingers. If the plane runs into an obstruction or starts to vibrate, your fingers can slide into the unprotected cutter head.

Block Plane

Designed for use on small surfaces, the block plane is necessarily operated with only one hand. Though convenient and useful, it is more dangerous than the larger, standard plane.

Operators tend to support the work with one hand while operating the block plane with the other. Any unexpected twist or movement can force the plane or the material to kick back and injure the operator. Keep your free hand well out of the way, in case the plane slips accidentally.

Maintaining Blades

- Avoid striking staples, nails, sand, or other foreign objects. The first step in maintenance is to make sure the work is free of obstructions.

- Keep blades in good condition and sharp. A sharp blade is safer to use than a dull blade that has to be held down and forced. A dull blade tends to float over the work and can bounce off, injuring the operator.

- Restore blades to original sharpness on a fine grit oilstone. Unless nicked or cracked, blades can be resharpened several times.

Changing Blades

Raising or replacing cutter blades takes time and patience. Blades must be the same weight and seated at the same height to prevent the cutter head from vibrating. Any deviation can cause the head to run off balance. Blades can fly out, injuring the operator or fellow workers.

Replacing cutter blades involves two steps: removing and installing.

Removing Blades

1) Disconnect the plane from the power source.

2) Turn the plane upside down and secure it in a fixed position.

3) Hold the cylinder head stationary by tapping a softwood wedge between the cutter head and the bearing (some tools are equipped with a locking device for this).

4) Loosen all the screws and lift out one blade and throat piece.

5) Turn the cutter head and repeat this procedure with other blades.

6) If necessary, clean parts thoroughly with kerosene.

Installing Blades

1) Replace one throat piece and blade.

2) Tighten the two end screws lightly.

3) Take a hardwood straight edge and use the outfeed table (back shoe) as a gauge. Raise or lower the blade until both ends are level with the outfeed table at the blade's highest point of revolution.

4) Tighten up the remaining screws.

5) Set the rest of the blades in the same way.

6) Turn the cylinder head and make sure that all blades are the same height.

7) Tighten up all the screws.

8) Doublecheck the height of all blades. Tightening can sometimes shift the set.

9) Doublecheck all the screws.

10) Turn the tool right side up and plug it in.

11) Hold the tool in both hands with the cutter blades facing away from you and switch it on.

Operation

- Always disconnect the plane from the power source before adjusting or changing blades or cutter head.

- Make sure that blades at their highest point of revolution are exactly flush with the outfeed table for safe, efficient operation (*Figure 139*).

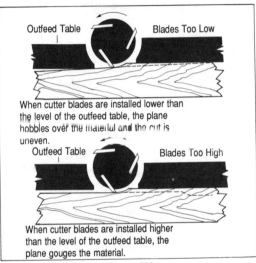

Outfeed Table — Blades Too Low

When cutter blades are installed lower than the level of the outfeed table, the plane hobbles over the material and the cut is uneven.

Outfeed Table — Blades Too High

When cutter blades are installed higher than the level of the outfeed table, the plane gouges the material.

Figure 139

- Support work securely for safety and accuracy.

- When planing doors and large pieces of plywood, use a jack (Figure *140*) to secure material and keep edges clear of dirt and grit.

- When using an electric block plane, clamp or fasten the workpiece whenever possible. Keep your free hand well away from plane and material.

- When using the standard power plane, adjust the edge guide to provide desired guidance.

- Adjust depth of cut to suit the type and width of wood to be planed.

- To start a cut, rest the infeed table (front shoe) firmly on the material with cutter head slightly behind the edge of the material. After finishing a cut, hold both hands on the plane until motor stops.

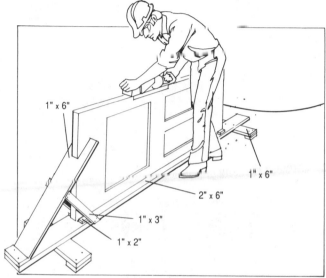

Figure 140
Door Jack

Routers

With special guides and bits, the portable electric router can be used to cut dadoes, grooves, mortises, dovetail joints, moldings, and internal or external curves. Carpenters find routers especially useful for mortising stair stringers and recessing hinges and lockplates on doors.

The router motor operates at very high speed (up to 25,000 rpm) and turns clockwise. Components are shown in *Figure 141*.

> **WARNING** The speed and power of the router require that it be operated with both hands.

When starting a router with a trigger switch in the handle, keep both hands on the tool to absorb the counterclockwise starting torque.

When starting a router with a toggle switch on top of the motor, hold the router firmly with one hand and switch on power with the other, then put both hands on the tool for control and accuracy.

Always wear eye protection.

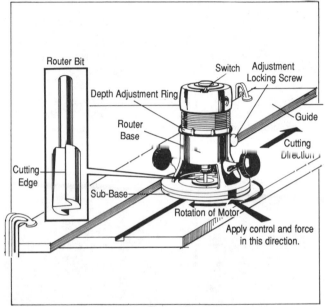

Figure 141
Router Parts and Operation

Operation

• Always support and secure the work in a fixed position by mechanical means such as a vise or clamps. Never try to hold the work down with your hand or knee. Never rely on a second person to hold the material. Human grip is no match for the torque and kickback that a router can generate.

• Make sure that the bit is securely mounted in the chuck and the base is tight.

- Set the base on the work, template, or guide and make sure that the bit can rotate freely before switching on the motor.

- For work along edges such as bevels and moldings, make sure that the cutting edge of the router bit contacts the material to the *left* of the cutting direction (*Figure 142*). Otherwise the router will kick back or fly away from you.

- When routing outside edges, guide the router around the work counterclockwise (*Figure 143*). Splinters left at corners by routing *across* the grain will be removed by the next pass *with* the grain.

- Feed the router bit into the material at a firm but controllable speed. There is no rule on how fast to cut. When working with softwood, the router can sometimes be moved as fast as it can go. Cutting may be very slow, however, with hardwood, knotty or twisted wood, and larger bits.

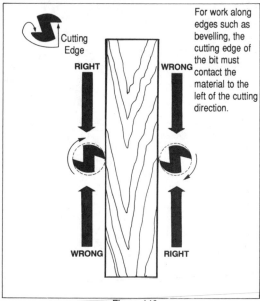

Figure 142

- For an indication of safe speed, listen to the motor. When the router is fed into the material too slowly, the motor makes a high-pitched whine. When the router is pushed too hard, the motor makes a low growling noise. Each situation can cause burnout or kickback.

- When the type of wood or size of bit necessitates slow going, make two or more passes to prevent the router from burning out or kicking back.

- If you're not sure about depth of cut or how many passes to make, test the router on a piece of scrap similar to the work.

- When the cut is complete, switch off power and keep both hands on the router until the motor stops. In lifting the tool from the work, avoid contact with the bit.

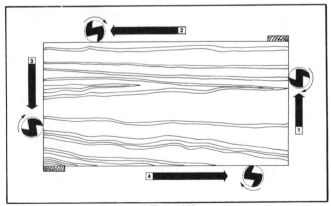

Figure 143

21 POWER TOOLS - SAWS

The saws covered in this chapter are

— circular   — quick-cut
— sabre   — table
— chain   — radial arm.
— chop

Basic Saw Safety

- Wear protective clothing and equipment (see Chapter 6). Eye protection is essential.

- Where saws are used in confined spaces or for prolonged periods, wear hearing protection.

- Where ventilation is inadequate, wear a dust mask for protection against dust. Over time, exposure to dust from particle board and other materials may cause respiratory problems.

- With electric saws operated outdoors or in wet locations, you must use a ground fault circuit interrupter.

- Never wear loose clothing, neck chains, scarves, or anything else that can get caught in the saw.

- Leave safety devices in place and intact on the saw. Never remove, modify, or defeat guards. Keep free hand away from blade (*Figure 144*).

- Always change and adjust blades with the power OFF. Disconnect electric saws from the power source before making changes or adjustments.

Circular Handsaws

The two models most often used on construction sites are illustrated. The main difference between the two lies in the drive action. The worm-drive saw has gears arranged so that the blade runs parallel to the motor shaft. The direct-drive saw has the blade at a right angle to the motor shaft.

The worm-drive saw periodically requires special gear oil to keep the inner gears lubricated. This requirement is usually eliminated in the direct-drive saw, which has sealed bearings and gears.

Both saws must be inspected regularly for defects and operated and maintained in accordance with manufacturers' recommendations.

Figure 144

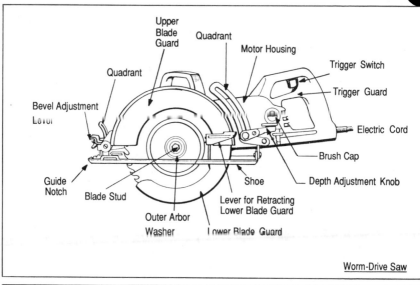

Upper Blade Guard

Quadrant

Quadrant

Motor Housing

Trigger Switch

Trigger Guard

Bevel Adjustment Lever

Electric Cord

Brush Cap

Guide Notch

Blade Stud

Shoe

Depth Adjustment Knob

Outer Arbor Washer

Lever for Retracting Lower Blade Guard

Lower Blade Guard

Worm-Drive Saw

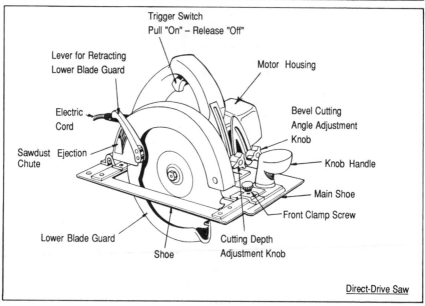

Trigger Switch
Pull "On" – Release "Off"

Lever for Retracting Lower Blade Guard

Motor Housing

Electric Cord

Bevel Cutting Angle Adjustment Knob

Sawdust Ejection Chute

Knob Handle

Main Shoe

Front Clamp Screw

Lower Blade Guard

Shoe

Cutting Depth Adjustment Knob

Direct-Drive Saw

232

Safety Features

Sawdust Ejection Chute This feature prevents sawdust from collecting in front of the saw and obscuring the cutting line. The operator can continue cutting without having to stop the saw and clear away sawdust.

Clutch Some worm-drive saws are equipped with a clutch to prevent kickback. Kickback occurs when a saw meets resistance and violently backs out of the work. The clutch action allows the blade shaft to continue turning when the blade meets resistance. Blade stud and friction washer can be adjusted to provide kickback protection for cutting different materials. Check friction washers for wear.

Brake An electric brake on some circular saws stops the blade from coasting once the switch is released. This greatly reduces the danger of accidental contact.

Trigger Safety On some light-duty saws a latch prevents the operator from accidentally starting the motor. The trigger on the inside of the handle cannot be pressed without first pressing a latch on the outside of the handle. On heavy-duty saws a bar under the trigger switch helps to prevent accidental starting.

Blades

Blades should be sharpened or changed frequently to prolong saw life, increase production, and reduce operator fatigue. The sides of the teeth on a dull or abused blade will turn blue from overheating. Such blades should be discarded or reconditioned.

Before changing or adjusting blades, disconnect the saw from the power source.

Take care to choose the right blade for the job. Blades are available in a variety of styles and tooth sizes. Combination blades (rip and crosscut) are the most widely used.

Ensure that arbor diameter and blade diameter are proper for the saw.

Because all lumber is not new, make sure it is clean and free of nails. This precaution not only prolongs blade life but may also prevent serious injury.

Take special care to ensure that blades are installed in the proper rotational direction (*Figure 145*). Remember that electrical circular handsaws cut with an upward motion. The teeth visible between the upper and lower guard should be pointing toward the front of the saw. Most models have a directional arrow on both blade and guard to serve as a guide.

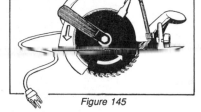

Figure 145

Blade Guards

Never operate an electric saw with the lower guard tied or wedged open. The saw may kick back and cut you, or another worker may pick up the saw and — not knowing that the guard is pinned back — sustain an injury.

Accidents have also occurred when the operator forgot that the blade is exposed and put the saw on the floor. The blade, still in motion, forces the saw to move, cutting anything in its path.

Make sure that the lower guard returns to its proper position after a cut. Never operate a saw with a defective guard retracting lever.

On most saws the lower guard is spring-loaded and correct tension in the spring will automatically close the guard. However, a spring weakened by use and wear can allow the guard to remain open after cutting. This creates a potential for injury if the operator inadvertently rests a still turning blade against his leg after finishing a cut. Always maintain complete control of the saw until the blade stops turning.

Choosing the Proper Blade

For safety, saw operators must understand the different designs and uses of blades (*Figure 146*). Blades unsuited for the job can be as hazardous as dull blades. For instance, a saw fitted with the wrong blade for the job can run hot so quickly that blade tension changes and creates a wobbly motion. The saw may kick back dangerously before the operator can switch it off.

Resharpened blades can be substantially reduced in diameter — for instance, from nine to eight inches. Make sure that the blade diameter and arbor diameter are proper for the saw.

Carbide-Tipped Blades — Take special care not to strike metal when using a carbide-tipped blade. The carbide tips can come loose and fly off, ruining the blade and injuring the operator. Inspect the blade regularly for cracked or missing tips.

Crosscut Blade — The bevelled sharp-pointed teeth are designed to cut the crossgrain in wood. Size and bevel of the teeth are important factors in cutting different woods. Softwood requires bigger teeth to carry off the sawdust. Hardwood requires fine teeth with many cutting edges. Note the different angles and edges needed for cutting hardwood and softwood.

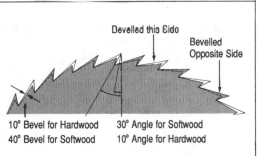

Bevelled this Side

Bevelled Opposite Side

10° Bevel for Hardwood
40° Bevel for Softwood

30° Angle for Softwood
10° Angle for Hardwood

Ripsaw Blade — The flat sharp teeth are designed to cut the long grain in wood. They are neither bevelled nor needle-pointed. Needle-pointed teeth would get clogged and the blade would become overheated. Never use a ripsaw blade for crosscutting or for cutting plywood. The material can jam and overheat the blade or splinter in long slivers that may seriously injure the operator.

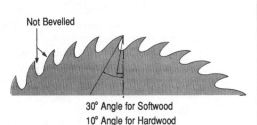

Not Bevelled

30° Angle for Softwood
10° Angle for Hardwood

Combination Blade — This blade combines features of the crosscut and ripsaw blades. It can be used for crosscutting and ripping, or for cutting plywood. Carpenters on construction sites prefer the combination blade for rough woodwork such as stud walls and formwork because they don't have to change blades. The teeth are alternately bevelled and have a straight front. The heel of each tooth is not lower than the heel of the tooth on either side of it.

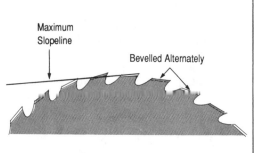

Maximum Slopeline

Bevelled Alternately

Standard Combination or Mitre Blade — This type is mainly used by trim carpenters. It includes teeth for crosscutting, raker teeth for ripping, and deep gullets for carrying off sawdust. The blade can be used for cutting both hardwood and softwood and for mitring.

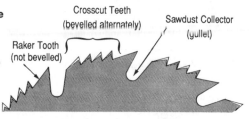

Crosscut Teeth (bevelled alternately)

Sawdust Collector (gullet)

Raker Tooth (not bevelled)

Figure 146

Changing, Adjusting, and Setting Blades

When changing blades, take the following precautions.

1. Disconnect the saw from the power source.

2. Place the saw blade on a piece of scrap lumber and press down until the teeth dig into the wood (*Figure 147*). This prevents the blade from turning when the locking nut is loosened or tightened. Some machines are provided with a mechanical locking device.

3. Make sure that keys and adjusting wrenches are removed before operating the saw.

Proper adjustment of cutting depth holds blade friction to a minimum, removes sawdust from the cut, and results in cool cutting.

The blade should project the depth of one full tooth below the material to be cut (*Figure 148*). When using carbide-tipped blades or mitre blades let only half a tooth project below the material.

If the blade is to run freely in the kerf (saw cut), teeth must be set properly, that is, bent alternately (*Figure 149*). The setting of teeth differs from one·type of blade to another. Finer-toothed blades require less set than rougher-toothed blades. Generally, teeth should be alternately bent 1/2 times the thickness of the blade.

Sharp blades with properly set teeth will reduce the chance of wood binding. They will also prevent the saw from overheating and kicking back.

Cutting

Place the material to be cut on a rigid support such as a bench or two or more sawhorses. Make sure that the blade will clear the supporting surface. The wide part of the saw shoe should rest on the supported side of the cut if possible.

Plywood is one of the most difficult materials to cut with any type of saw. The overall size of the sheet and the internal stresses released by cutting are the main causes of difficulty. Large sheets should be supported in at least three places, with one support next to the cut.

Short pieces of material should not be held by hand. Use some form of clamping to hold the material down when cutting it (*Figure 150*).

NEVER use your leg as a work bench. Too many operators have ended up seriously injured by this careless act.

The material to be cut should be placed with its good side *down*, if possible. Because the blade cuts upward into the material, any splintering will be on the side which is uppermost.

Use just enough force to let the blade cut without labouring. Hardness and toughness can vary in the same piece of material, and a knotty or wet section can put a heavier load on the saw. When this happens, reduce pressure to keep the speed of the blade constant. Forcing the saw beyond its capacity will result in rough and inaccurate cuts. It will also overheat the motor and the saw blade.

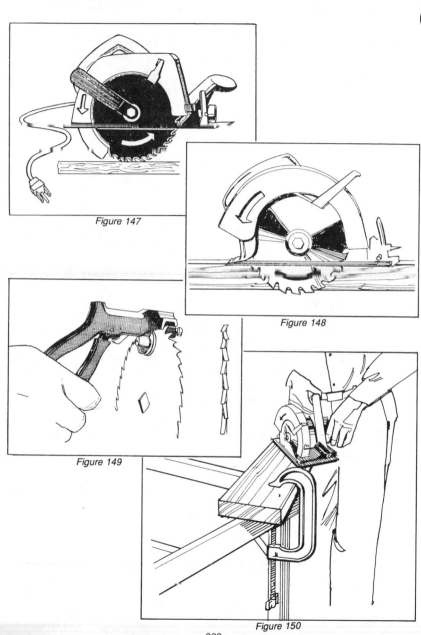

Figure 147

Figure 148

Figure 149

Figure 150

Take the saw to the material. Never place the saw in a fixed, upside-down position and feed material into it. Use a table saw instead.

If the cut gets off line, don't force the saw back onto line. Withdraw the blade and either start over on the same line or begin on a new line.

If cutting right-handed, keep the cord on that side of your body. Stand to one side of the cutting line. **Never reach under the material being cut.**

Always keep your free hand on the *long* side of the lumber and clear of the saw. Maintain a firm, well-balanced stance, particularly when working on uneven footing.

Plywood, wet lumber, and lumber with a twisted grain tend to tighten around a blade and may cause kickbacks. Kickbacks occur when an electric saw stalls suddenly and jerks back toward the operator. The momentarily exposed blade may cause severe injury

Use extreme caution and don't relax your grip on the saw.

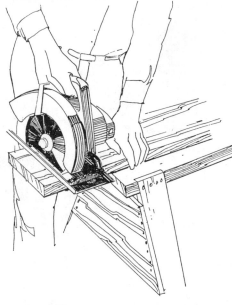

Pocket Cutting

1. Tilt saw forward.

2. Rest front of shoe on wood.

3. Retract lower guard

4. Lower saw until front teeth almost touch wood.

5. Release guard to rest on wood.

6. Switch on the saw.

7. Keep the saw tilted forward and push it down and forward with even pressure, gradually lowering it until shoe rests flat on wood.

8. Follow all these steps with extreme care.

Sabre Saws

The sabre saw, or portable jigsaw (*Figure 151*), is designed for cutting external or internal contours. The saw should not be used for continuous or heavy cutting that can be done more safely and efficiently with a circular saw.

The stroke of the sabre saw is about 1/2 inch for the light-duty model and about 3/4 inch for the heavy duty model. The one-speed saw operates at approximately 2,500 strokes per minute. The variable-speed saw can operate from one to 2,500 strokes per minute.

The reciprocating saw (*Figure 152*) is a heavier type of sabre saw with a larger and more rugged blade. The tool is often used by drywall and acoustical workers to cut holes in ceilings and walls. Equipped with a small swivel base, the saw can be used in corners or free-hand in hard-to-reach places. The reciprocating saw must be held with both hands to absorb vibrations and to avoid accidental contact.

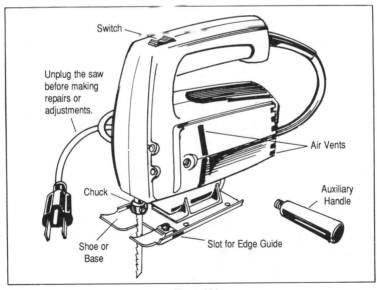

Figure 151
Sabre Saw

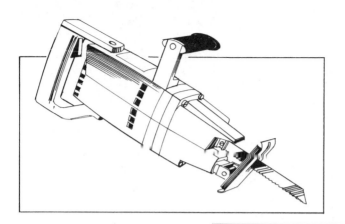

Figure 152
Reciprocating Saw

Use caution when cutting through
walls. Beware of electrical wiring
and other services in or behind
the wall.

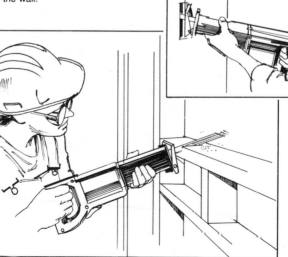

Choosing the Proper Blade

Various blades, ranging from 17 to 32 teeth per inch, are available for cutting different materials. For the rough cutting of stock such as softwood and composition board, a blade with 7 teeth per inch will cut the fastest. For all-round work with most types of wood, a blade with 10 teeth per inch is satisfactory.

Cutting

The sabre saw cuts on the upstroke. Splintering will therefore occur on the top side of the material being cut. Consequently, the good side should be facing down. Degree of splintering depends on the type of blade, the vibration of the material, and the feed of the saw.

To avoid vibration, the material should be clamped or otherwise secured and supported as close to the cutting line as possible. If the material vibrates excessively or shifts during cutting, the saw can run out of control, damaging the blade and injuring the operator.

• Before starting a cut make sure that the saw will not make contact with clamps, vise, workbench, or other support.

• Never reach under the material being cut.

• Never lay down the saw until the motor has stopped.

• Do not try to cut curves so sharp that the blade will twist and break.

• Always hold the base or shoe of the saw in firm contact with the material being cut.

> **WARNING**   When sawing into floors, ceilings, or walls, always check for plumbing and wiring.

External Cut   (*Figure 153*)

To start an external cut (from the outside in), place the front of the shoe on the material. Make sure that the blade is not in contact with the material or the saw will stall when the motor starts.

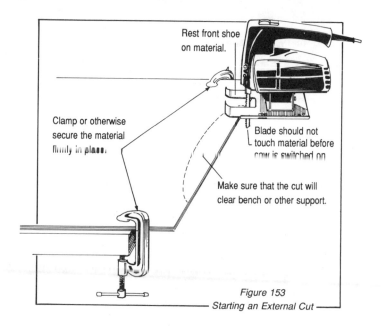

Rest front shoe
on material.

Clamp or otherwise
secure the material
firmly in place.

Blade should not
touch material before
saw is switched on.

Make sure that the cut will
clear bench or other support.

Figure 153
Starting an External Cut

Hold the saw firmly and switch it on. Feed the blade slowly into the material and maintain an even pressure. When the cut is complete, do not lay down the saw until the motor has stopped.

Inside Cuts *(Figure 154)*

To start an inside cut (pocket cut), first drill a lead hole slightly larger than the saw blade. With the saw switched off, insert the blade into the hole until the shoe tests firmly on the material. Do not let the blade touch the material until the saw has been switched on.

When absolutely necessary, it is possible to start an inside cut without drilling a lead hole first. To do this, rest the front edge of the shoe on the material with the saw tipped backward. Keep the blade out of contact with the material.

Switch on the saw and slowly feed the blade into the material while lowering the back edge of the shoe. When the shoe rests flat on the material and the blade is completely through, proceed with the cut. Any deviation from this procedure can cause the blade to break and injure the operator or workers nearby.

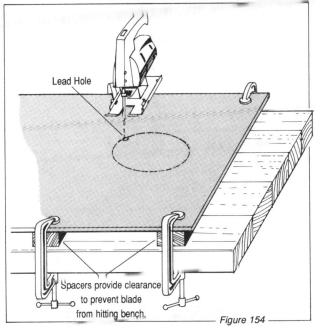

Lead Hole

Spacers provide clearance
to prevent blade
from hitting bench.

Figure 154
Starting an Inside Cut

While the motor is running, never try to insert a blade into, or withdraw a blade from, a cut or a lead hole.

Never reach under the material being cut.

Chain Saws

Each year in Ontario, construction workers are injured while using chain saws. Generally the injuries result from two types of accidents:

1) the operator makes accidental contact with the revolving chain
2) the operator is struck by the object being cut, usually a tree or heavy limb.

Many of these injuries are serious.

While the chain saw is relatively easy to operate, it can be lethal. As with all high-speed cutting tools, it demands the full attention of even the trained and experienced operator.

245

Requirements

Chain saws can be powered by electric motors (*Figure 155*) or gasoline engines (*Figure 156*).

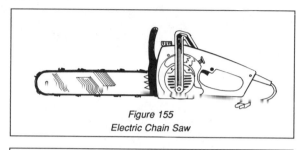

Figure 155
Electric Chain Saw

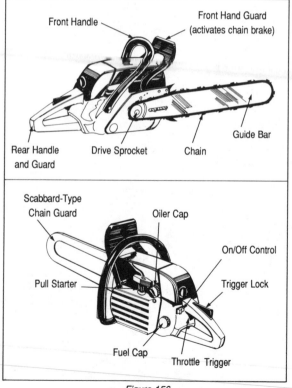

Front Handle

Front Hand Guard
(activates chain brake)

Rear Handle
and Guard

Drive Sprocket

Chain

Guide Bar

Scabbard-Type
Chain Guard

Oiler Cap

On/Off Control

Pull Starter

Trigger Lock

Fuel Cap

Throttle Trigger

Figure 156
Gasoline Chain Saw

Both saws are designed to provide fast cutting action with a minimum of binding in the cut, even though wood may be sap-filled or wet. Both afford relatively the same performance in relation to their respective horsepower and are equipped with similar controls and safety devices.

Regulations require that chain saws used on construction must be equipped with a chain brake. Make sure that the saw is equipped with a chain brake mechanism, and not simply a hand guard, which is similar in appearance.

Regulations require that chain saws used on construction must be equipped with "anti-kickback" chains. Called safety chains (*Figure 157*) by the manufacturers, these chains incorporate design features intended to minimize kickback while maintaining cutting performance.

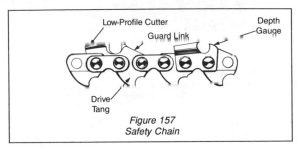

Figure 157
Safety Chain

Protective Clothing and Equipment

- Eye protection in the form of plastic goggles is recommended. A faceshield attached to the hard hat will not provide the total eye protection of close-fitting goggles.

- Leather gloves offer a good grip on the saw, protect the hands, and absorb some vibration. Gloves with ballistic nylon reinforcement on the back of the hand are recommended.

- Since most chain saws develop a high decibel rating (between 95 and 115 dBA depending on age and condition), hearing protection should be worn, especially during prolonged exposure.

- Trousers or chaps with sewn-in ballistic nylon pads provide excellent protection, particularly for the worker who regularly uses a chain saw.

Kickback

Kickback describes the violent motion of the saw that can result when a rotating chain is unexpectedly interrupted. The cutting chain's forward movement is halted and energy is transferred to the saw, throwing it back from the cut toward the operator.

The most common and probably most violent kickback occurs when contact is made in the "kickback zone" (*Figure 158*).

Contact in this zone makes the chain bunch up and try to climb out of the track. This most often happens when the saw tip makes contact with something beyond the cutting area such as a tree branch, log, or the ground.

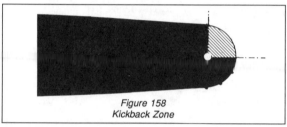

Figure 158
Kickback Zone

To minimize the risk of kickback

— use a low-profile safety chain
— run the saw at high rpm when cutting
— sharpen the chain to correct specifications
— set depth gauges to manufacturers' settings
— maintain correct chain tension
— hold the saw securely with both hands
— don't operate the saw when you are tired
— know where the bar tip is at all times
— don't allow the cut to close on the saw
— make sure the chain brake is functioning.

Starting

When starting, hold the saw firmly on the ground or other level support with the chain pointing away from your body and nearby obstructions. Use a quick, sharp motion on the starter pull (*Figure 159*). Never "drop start" the saw. This leaves only one hand to control a running saw and has resulted in leg cuts. Use the proper grip (*Figure 160*).

248

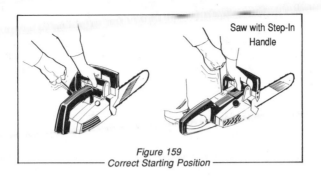

Figure 159
Correct Starting Position

Saw with Step-In Handle

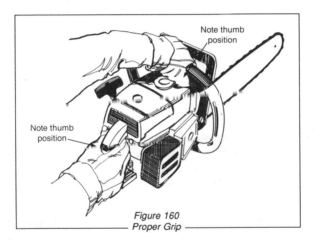

Note thumb position

Note thumb position

Figure 160
Proper Grip

Before moving from place to place, shut off the saw and walk with the guide bar pointed backwards. A trip or a stumble with a running saw can cause serious injury.

Site Hazards

• Take extra care when making pocket cuts (*Figure 161*). Start the cut with the underside of the chain tip, then work the saw down and back to avoid contact with the kickback zone. An alternative such as a sabre saw should be considered.

249

- Be particularly careful to avoid contact with nails, piping, and other metallic objects. This is especially important when making a pocket cut through framing lumber such as a subfloor or when cutting used lumber such as trench shoring, lagging, or blocking timbers.

- Use chain saws only to cut wood. They are not designed to cut other materials.

- When using a chain saw to trim rafter ends, take the following steps to avoid injury:

  — Cut **down** from the top of the rafter. Don't cut from underneath.

  — Use a safety belt, lanyard, and lifeline to prevent falls or work from a secure scaffold at eaves level.

  — The extension cord on an electric chain saw should be secured on the roof above the operator with enough working slack. This will prevent the weight of a long cord from pulling the operator off balance.

  — Keep both hands firmly on the saw.

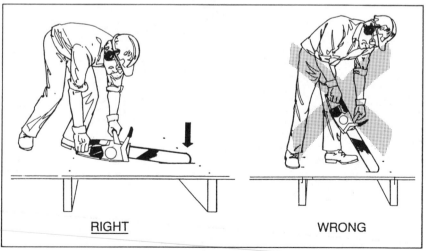

RIGHT   WRONG

Figure 161
Pocket Cuts

Maintenance

Well maintained cutting components are essential for safe operation. A dull or improperly filed chain will increase the risk of kickback.

- Inspect the drive links and the running groove in the guide bar for damage. A good practice is to replace both chain and bar when the bar is damaged.

- Select the proper size files for sharpening the chain. Two files are necessary:

  1) a flat file for adjusting depth gauge
  2) a round file of uniform diameter for sharpening cutters and maintaining drive links.

- You must choose the correct round file for your chain to avoid damaging the cutters. Consult the owner's manual or the supplier to be sure of file size.

- A round file used in combination with a file holder or, better yet, a precision filing guide will give the best results (*Figure 162*).

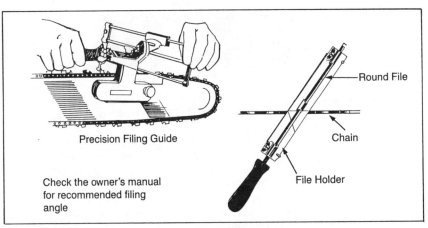

Precision Filing Guide

Check the owner's manual for recommended filing angle

Round File

Chain

File Holder

Figure 162
Sharpening Tools

Adjusting Chain Tension

- Follow manufacturer's instructions on chain tension.

- In general, the chain should move easily around the bar by hand without showing noticeable sag at the bottom (*Figure 163*).

- Be generous with chain lubricating oil. It is almost impossible to use too much. Most late model saws have automatic oilers but operators must still remember to fill the chain-oil reservoir.

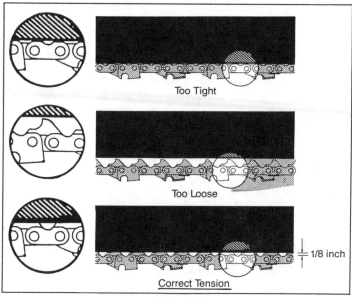

Too Tight

Too Loose

1/8 inch

Correct Tension

Figure 163
No Noticeable Sag

Chop Saws

Increasingly, carpenters and other trades are using chop (*Figure 164*) saws to cut various materials. These portable saws offer quick, efficient, and economical cutting.

Unfortunately like all power equipment, chop saws pose serious hazards for the unwary or untrained operator. Follow **Basic Saw Safety** and **Safety Basics** as for other power saws.

Most of these saws are equipped with abrasive wheels for quick cutting through metal studs and other material.

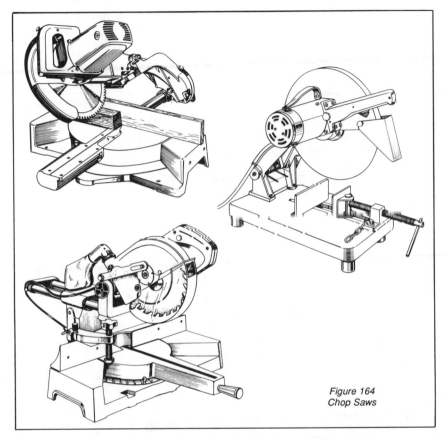

Figure 164
Chop Saws

- Select the proper abrasive cutting wheel for the material being cut. For metals, use aluminum oxide. For masonry, stone, and concrete, use silica carborundum.

- RPM of the saw should not exceed the recommended RPM printed on the blade label.

- The centre hole on the blade must fit the mandril and be snugly fastened in place with the proper washer and lock nut.

> **Warning** A loose or off-centre blade can shatter in use.

- Position material to be cut at 90 degrees to the blade. Support the other end to prevent the blade from binding.

- Do not rush cutting. Let the wheel cut without burning or jamming.

  When cutting is complete, let the blade stop before moving material.

- Maintain the saw in good repair with the blade guard in place and working smoothly. Tighten any loose parts and replace any broken or damaged ones.

- Don't try to adjust for length on downward cutting motion. Your hand could slide into the blade while it is spinning.

- With some large chop saws (*Figure 165*), additional precautions are required because of the tremendous torque the saws can develop.

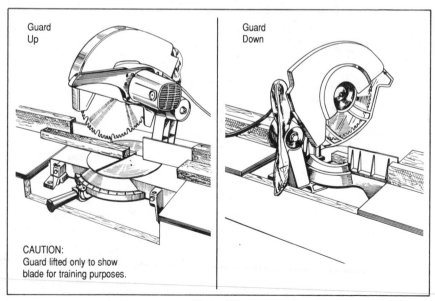

Guard
Up

Guard
Down

CAUTION:
Guard lifted only to show
blade for training purposes.

Figure 165
Some large chop saws may require additional precautions.

Quick-Cut Saws

Hand-held portable circular cut-off saws are commonly known as quick-cut saws in construction (Figure 166). They are widely used for cutting concrete, masonry products, sheet metal products (both steel and aluminum), and light steel sections such as angles and channels.

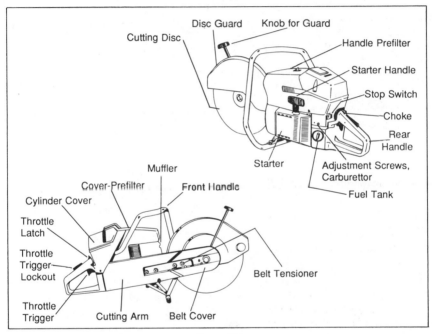

Figure 166

Hazards

Quick-cut saws are high-powered compared to similar tools. Hazards include high-speed blade rotation, blade exposure during operation, and exhaust from the internal combustion engine—the usual power source.

The saws also create clouds of dust when dry-cutting masonry and showers of hot sparks when cutting metal products, especially steel.

These hazards can result in cuts, kickbacks, exposure to carbon monoxide fumes, exposure to dusts (silica from concrete and masonry products in particular), burns, flying particles in the eye, and other injuries from flying material when work is not secured for cutting or when blades fly apart.

These hazards can be controlled by
- operators trained to use quick-cut saws properly and to wear the right protective equipment

- saws kept in good working condition, equipped with the proper blades or abrasive disks, and used with all guards in place

- work secured to keep it from shifting during cutting.

Training

Operators should be instructed in the care, maintenance, and operation of quick-cut saws. They should read the operating manual, review the major points, and receive both oral and written instruction.

The operating manual should be available on the job, not only for instruction but for ready reference when something goes wrong with the saw or it must be used for work outside the operator's experience.

Time spent on instruction will reduce accidents and injuries as well as prolong the service life of the saw.

As a minimum the operator should be instructed in
- care of the saw
- installing disks and blades
- mixing fuel and fuelling the saw
- starting the saw
- supporting and securing work to be cut
- proper cutting stance and grip
- proper cutting techniques for different material
- respiratory protection against dusts
- how to inspect and store abrasive disks.

Care

Quick-cut saws must be serviced and maintained in accordance with the manufacturer's instructions. Replacement parts should be those recommended by the manufacturer.

Cracked, broken, or worn parts should be replaced before the saw is used again. Guards and air-intakes should be cleaned regularly and often. Abrasive disks should be checked before installation and frequently during use. Correct excessive blade vibration before trying to make a cut.

In confined areas, make sure that ventilation is adequate. Gasoline-driven saws release carbon monoxide gas — odourless, colourless, and highly toxic.

Starting

Most of the following procedures are for gasoline-powered quick-cut saws—the type most commonly used in construction.

- Use caution when preparing the oil/gasoline mixture and when fuelling the saw. No smoking or ignition sources should be allowed in the area where fuel is mixed or tanks are filled.

- Fill the tank outdoors in a well ventilated space at least 3 metres from the area where the saw will be used. Spilled fuel should be wiped off the saw.

- Check the saw for leaks. Sometimes vibration makes gas lines leak.

- Carry the saw with the disk or blade removed and with the muffler away from you.

- Start the saw in an area clear of people and obstacles. Under no circumstances should anyone be standing in front of the saw as it starts or while it's running.

- Put the saw on a smooth hard surface for starting. The guard should be properly set for the type of cut beforehand.

- Assume a solid well-balanced stance. Do not wrap the starter cord around your hand—this can cause injury.

- Set one foot on the rear handle, put one hand on the top handle to lift the blade off the surface, and use the other hand to pull the starter cord (*Figure 167*).

257

Figure 167
Starting Position

- Avoid fuelling the saw on or near formwork. Gasoline spills are a fire hazard. Use a funnel to avoid spills.

Warning Always shut off saw while fuelling.

- Do not overfill the saw or run it without securing the fuel tank cap. Gasoline seeping from the tank can saturate your clothing and be ignited by sparks thrown off from metal cutting. Only use the cap supplied by the manufacturer.

- Once the saw is running, release the throttle and make sure the engine drops to idle without the disk or blade moving.

- Run the engine at full throttle and let the disk or blade run freely to make sure it turns on the arbor without wobbling or vibrating.

Support

One of the major hazards with quick-cut saws is failure to support and secure the work to be cut.

The saw is powerful enough to throw material around unless it is securely held and supported. Standing on material to hold it down is **not** recommended.

For repeated cuts of masonry or metal pieces, a jig is ideal for efficiency and safety. The jig should be designed and built to hold material in place after measurement without further manual contact (*Figure 168*).

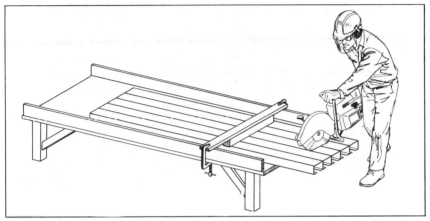

Figure 168
Jig for Cutting

Stance and Grip

The quick-cut saw is a heavy, powerful tool that must be held by hand. Operators need a secure stance with legs apart for balance and support. The saw should be held at a comfortable, balanced location in front of the operator.

Grip the saw firmly with one hand on each handle. Hold your forward arm straight to keep the saw from kicking back or climbing out of the cut (*Figure 169*).

Figure 169
Cutting Stance and Grip

Cutting

Although skill in handling the quick-cut saw can only be learned through practice, some safety considerations and operating techniques must always be kept in mind, even by the most experienced operators.

Work should be supported so that the disk or blade will not bind in the cut. Support heavier materials on both sides of the cut so the cut piece will not drop or roll onto the operator's foot. Lighter materials can generally be allowed to fall. In all cases the cut should be as close as possible to the supporting surface (*Figure 170*).

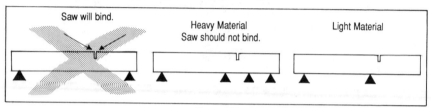

Figure 170
Support for Different Cuts

Kickback and Pull-In

Kickback can happen extremely fast and with tremendous power. If the segment of the disk or blade shown in *Figure 171* contacts the work, the disk or blade starts to climb out of the cut and can throw the saw up and back toward the operator with great force.

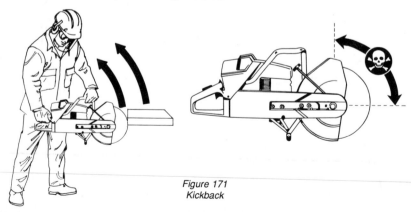

Figure 171
Kickback

For cutting, keep the throttle wide open. Ease the blade down onto the cut line. Don't drop or jam the blade down hard. Move the saw slowly back and forth in the cut.

Hold the saw so that disk or blade is at right angles to the work and use only the cutting edge of the disk or blade (*Figure 172*). Never use the side of a disk for cutting. A worn disk will almost certainly shatter and may cause severe injury.

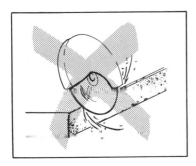

Figure 172
Saw at Right Angles to Material

Don't force the saw to one side of the cut. This will bend the disk or blade and cause it to bind, possibly to break.

Water cooling is recommended for cutting masonry materials. It prolongs disk life and reduces dust exposure.

Keep pressure on the saw reasonably light. Although more pressure may be necessary for hard materials, it can cause an abrasive disk to chip or go "out of round." This in turn will make the saw vibrate. If lowering the feed pressure does not stop vibration, replace the disk.

Don't carry the saw any distance with the engine running. Stop the engine and carry the saw with the muffler away from you.

To avoid kickback, take the following steps.

- Secure and support the material at a comfortable position for cutting. Make sure that material will not move, shift, or pinch the blade or disk during cutting.

- Keep steady balance and solid footing when making a cut.

- Use both hands to control the saw. Maintain a firm grip with thumb and fingers encircling the handles.

- Never let the upper quarter segment of blade or disk contact the material.

- Run the saw at full throttle.

- Do not cut above chest height.

- When reentering a cut, do so without causing blade or disk to pinch.

Pull-in occurs when the lower part of the disk or blade is stopped suddenly—for instance, by a cut closing up and binding. The saw pitches forward and can pull the operator off balance.

To protect yourself against kickback and pull-in, maintain a well-balanced stance and two-handed grip on the saw at all times when cutting.

Protective Equipment

In addition to the standard equipment mandatory on construction sites, operators of quick-cut saws should wear snug-fitting clothing, hearing protection, eye and face protection, and heavy-duty leather gloves (*Figure 173*).

The dry cutting of masonry or concrete products calls for respiratory protection as well. See Chapter 6.

For general dust hazards a half-mask cartridge respirator with NIOSH-approval for dust, mist, and fumes (TC21C) should provide adequate protection when properly fitted and worn by a cleanshaven person.

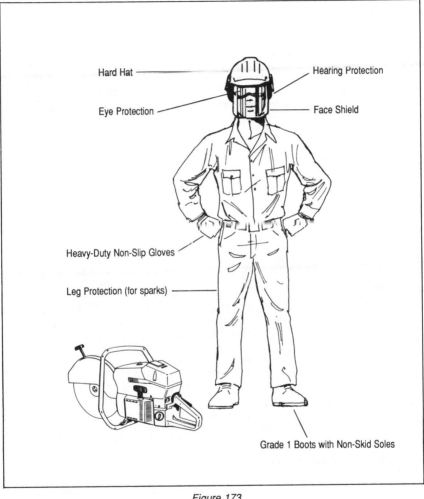

Hard Hat

Eye Protection

Hearing Protection

Face Shield

Heavy-Duty Non-Slip Gloves

Leg Protection (for sparks)

Grade 1 Boots with Non-Skid Soles

Figure 173
Protective Equipment

Disks and Blades

Disks and blades are available in three basic types:
- abrasive disks
- diamond-tipped blades
- carbide-tipped blades.

Use only the disks and blades compatible with your saw and rated for its maximum rpm. If you have any doubts, consult the operating manual or a reputable supplier.

Abrasive Disks

These disks are a combination of abrasives and organic binders. Reinforced abrasive disks contain fabrics to prevent the disk from flying apart when damaged or cracked.

Abrasive Disks - Types and Uses

Type	Uses	Materials
Concrete	All-around use, most economical for cutting concrete and masonry. **Water-cooling** is recommended to increase disk life and reduce dust.	Concrete, stone, masonry products, cast iron, aluminum, copper, brass, cables, hard rubber, plastics
Metal	Primarily for steel, not suited for masonry products. Water-cooling is not recommended with metal abrasive disks.	Steel, steel alloys, other hard metals such as monel and iron

Diamond Disks and Blades

Diamond disks are normally used with water cooling. Recently, however, diamond blades are available for dry cutting, which may be necessary to avoid staining some masonry products.

When dry-cutting with a diamond blade, let the blade cool for 10-15 seconds every 40-60 seconds. This can be done simply by pulling the saw out of the cut.

Diamond Disks and Blades - Types and Uses

Type	Uses	Materials
Diamond Abrasive Disk	Faster cuts than with other abrasive disks and creates less dust. **Water-cooling** is absolutely necessary to prevent heat build-up that can make the disk disintegrate.	Stone, all masonry and concrete products. Not recommended for metals.
Dry-Cut Diamond Blade	Fast cuts, lots of dust, very expensive. Let blade cool for 10-15 seconds every 40-60 seconds. Continuous cutting will damage the blade.	Stone, all masonry and concrete products. Not recommended for metals.

Carbide-Tipped Blades

These blades must be used with care. If a carbide-tipped blade encounters material harder than what it is designed to cut, the tips may fly off.

A carbide-tipped blade used with a quick-cut saw **must** be designed for that purpose. It must also be used only to cut the materials specified by the manufacturer.

Inspection/Installation

Inspect disks and blades before installing them.

- Make sure that contact surfaces are flat, run true on the arbor, and are free of foreign material.

- Check that flanges are the correct size and not warped or sprung (*Figure 174*).

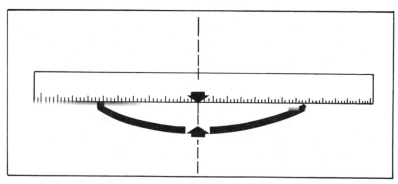

Figure 174
Check disk for warping.

- Check the label to make sure that the disk or blade is approved for use on high-speed chop saws and has a rated rpm suitable to the saw being used. A periodic service check may be necessary to ensure that the rpm still meets the manufacturer's requirement.

- Inspect the disk or blade for damage. Abrasive disks tapped lightly with a piece of wood should ring true. If the sound is dull or flat, the disk is damaged and should be discarded.

- Make sure that diamond or carbide tips are all in place. Do not use diamond or carbide-tipped blades or disks if any tips are missing.

- Do not drop abrasive disks. Discard any disk that has been dropped.

- Use the proper bushing on the arbor so that the disk runs true on the shaft without wobbling or vibrating.

- Discard badly worn disks that are uneven or "out of round."

Table Saws

Types

The table saw most often used in construction is the 10-inch belt-driven tilting arbor saw. The dimension refers to the diameter of the saw blade recommended by the manufacturer.

Although some saws are direct-drive (*Figure 175*), with the blade mounted right on the motor arbor, most are belt-driven (*Figure 176*).

Both types are equipped with a fixed table top and an arbor that can be raised, lowered, or tilted to one side for cutting at different depths and angles.

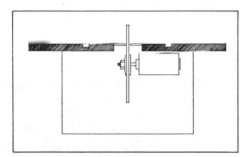

Figure 175
Direct-Drive Table Saw

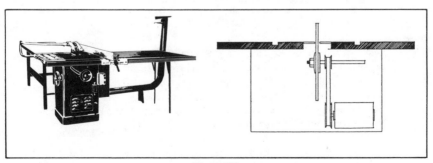

Figure 176
Belt-Driven Table Saw

Basket Guards

Basket guards may be fastened to the splitter or hinged to either side of the saw on an L-shaped or S-shaped arm (*Figure 177*).

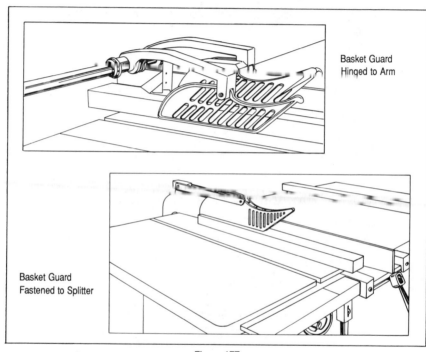

Basket Guard
Hinged to Arm

Basket Guard
Fastened to Splitter

Figure 177
Basket Guards

Basket guards can protect the operator from sawdust, splinters, and accidental contact with the blade. Keep the basket guard in place for normal operations such as straight and bevel ripping and mitre cutting. When the guard is removed to permit cutting of tenons, finger joints, rabbets, and similar work, use accessories such as feather boards, holding jigs, push sticks, and saw covers.

Figure 178 shows a split basket guard with a see-through cover. One side can be moved sideways for a blade tilted to 45 degrees. One side can be lifted up while the other remains as a protective cover.

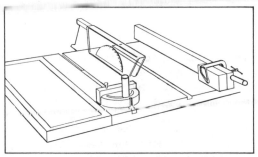

Figure 178
See-Through Plastic Basket Guard

Sheet metal baskets fastened to the splitter are less effective because the operator cannot see the saw blade.

Kickback

Kickback occurs when stock binds against the saw blade. The blade can fire the wood back at the operator with tremendous force, causing major injuries to abdomen, legs, and hands.

* Never stand directly behind the blade when cutting. Stand to one side. See that other workers stand clear as well.

* Make sure the rip fence is aligned for slightly more clearance behind the blade than in front. This will help prevent binding.

* Use a sharp blade with teeth properly set for the wood being cut. A dull or badly gummed blade will cause friction, overheating, and binding.

* Install a splitter to keep the kerf (cut) open behind the blade. Also effective are anti-kickback fingers attached to the splitter.

Splitters

Splitters prevent the kerf from closing directly behind the blade. Ideally, they should be slightly thinner than the saw blade and manufactured from high tensile steel.

Splitters are not always needed with carbide-tipped saw blades, whose relatively wide kerf may provide the desirable clearance. A wide kerf alone, however, is often not enough to keep some boards from closing behind the cut and binding against the blade.

In general, it is impossible to predict how a board will behave during ripping. It may remain straight, presenting no problems. On the other hand, the release of internal stresses may make the two ripped portions behind the blade either close up or spread apart.

Figure 179 shows a disappearing splitter with anti-kickback fingers. It can be pushed down when in the way of a workpiece and pulled up when necessary after the machine has been shut off.

Figure 179
Disappearing Splitter
with Anti-Kickback Fingers

Roller Stand

Operators risk injury trying to maintain control over long pieces of stock singlehandedly, especially if the stock begins to bind on the blade and kick back.

A roller stand (*Figure 180*) provides the needed support. Adjust it to a height slightly lower than the saw table to allow for sagging of the material. Be sure to set up the stand so the roller axis is at 90 degrees to the blade. Otherwise, the roller could pull the stock off to one side and cause binding.

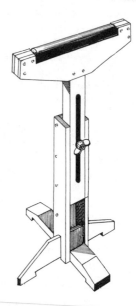

Figure 180
Roller Stand

Whatever the design, a support stand should be standard equipment in every carpentry and millwork shop. It can be used as an extension to a workbench, jointer, or bandsaw and is especially important with the table saw.

Extensions

Made of wood or metal, table top extensions installed behind and to both sides of the machine can make the cutting of large sheets of plywood and long stock safer and more efficient.

In most cases a space must be provided between extension and saw top for adjusting the basket guard and allowing scrap to fall clear.

Blades

Table saw blades are basically similar to those for circular saws.

The teeth on carbide-tipped, hollow-ground, and taper blades do not need setting (*Figure 181*).

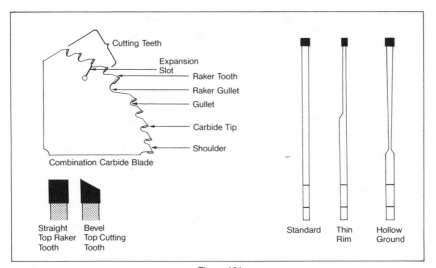

Figure 181
Carbide-Tipped Blades

Blade Adjustment

Proper adjustment of cutting depth holds blade friction to a minimum, removes sawdust from the cut, and results in cool cutting.

Sharp blades with properly set teeth will keep the work from binding and the blade from overheating and kicking back.

The blade should project the depth of one full tooth above the material to be cut. When using carbide-tipped blades or mitre blades let only half a tooth project above the material.

Blade Speed

The right cutting speed is important. The blade should turn at the correct rpm to yield the recommended cutting speed.

When not in motion, saw blades, especially large blades, are usually not perfectly flat because of internal tensions. At the right operating speeds, however, the blades straighten out as a result of centrifugal force and cut smoothly at full capacity.

Blades running too fast or too slow tend to start wobbling either before or during a cut. If cutting continues, the blade will overheat and may cause kickback, damage the equipment, and injure the operator.

Rip Fence

The rip fence is used mainly to guide the stock and maintain correct width of cut. The fence on small saws is usually clamped down at both the front and back of the table by pushing down a lever or turning a knob. Adjust the fence slightly wider at the back to let the wood spread out behind the cut and reduce the risk of kickback.

Many carpenters add a piece of hardwood to the rip fence in order to rip thin pieces of wood and make dadoes and rabbets. The auxiliary fence can be set close to the cutters with the risk of contact between the blade and the steel fence.

Pushsticks

Narrow pieces can be cut safely and efficiently with the help of pushsticks (*Figure 182*), which should be painted or otherwise marked to prevent loss.

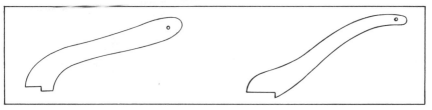

Figure 182
Pushsticks

To rip narrow, short pieces, a push block is the right choice (*Figure 183*). The shoe holds the material down on the table while the heel moves the stock forward and keeps it from kicking back.

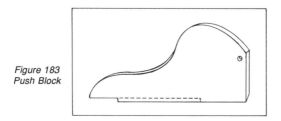

Figure 183
Push Block

Different designs of pushsticks are required for cutting different kinds of stock.

The heel of the pushstick should be deep enough to prevent it from slipping and strong enough to feed the stock through the saw.

Feather Boards

Another way of ripping narrow stock safely relies on one or two feather boards (*Figure 184*). A feather board clamped immediately in front of the saw blade will provide side pressure to the stock without causing binding and kickback. Use a push block to feed stock all the way through.

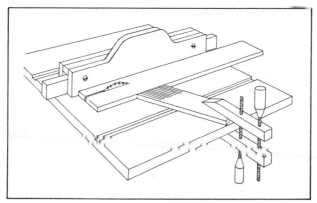

Clamp second
feather board to
auxiliary rip fence.

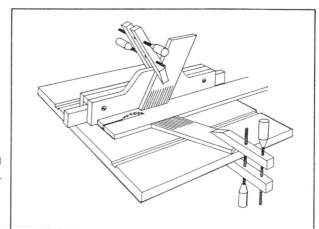

Clamp feather board
in front of saw blade.

Figure 184
Feather Boards

Operation

- Follow **Basic Saw Safety** (page 230).

- Keep the floor around the saw clear of scrap and sawdust to prevent slipping and tripping.

- Always stop the machine before making adjustments. Before making major adjustments, always disconnect the main power supply.

- Select a sharp blade suitable for the job.

- Use the safety devices such as pushsticks and feather boards recommended in this chapter.

- Make sure nobody stands in line with a revolving blade.

- Don't let anyone or anything distract you when you are operating the saw.

- Whenever possible, keep your fingers folded in a fist rather than extended as you feed work into the saw.

- Never reach around, over, or behind a running blade to control the stock.

- Follow manufacturer's recommendations in matching motor size to the saw. Underpowered saws can be unsafe.

- Table saws should be properly grounded. Check the power supply for ground and always use a ground fault circuit interrupter. This is mandatory for saws used outdoors or in wet locations.

- Table saws should be equipped with an on/off switch so power can be shut off quickly in an emergency.

- A magnetic starter switch is preferable to a mechanical toggle because it prevents the saw from starting up again unexpectedly after an interruption in power.

- When purchasing a new table saw, try to get one equipped with an electric brake. The brake stops blade rotation within seconds of the operator turning off the saw. The reduced risk of injury is worth the extra cost.

- Extension cords should be of sufficient wire gauge for the voltage and amperage required by the saw and for the length of the run.

Radial Arm Saws

The motor and blade of the radial arm saw are suspended above the table (*Figure 185*). Because the motor and blade assembly can be locked in different positions and can travel during the cut, the operator must pay special attention to keeping fingers and hands clear.

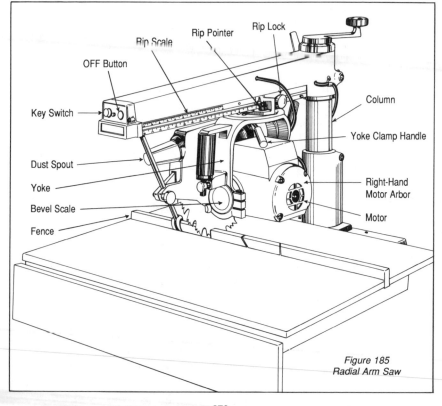

*Figure 185
Radial Arm Saw*

Injuries involving radial arm saws tend to be serious. By using appropriate guards and procedures, however, operators can safely use the saw for crosscuts, mitre cuts, ripping, and dadoes.

Set-Up

- The saw must be adequately powered for the work, especially for cutting thick hardwood.

- The saw should be installed in a well-lit area out of the way of traffic, with enough space to store and handle long lengths of wood. Locating the machine with its back to a wall or partition can help to keep flying pieces from hitting anyone.

- Where possible, mark the floor with yellow warning lines to keep other personnel back from the saw.

- Make sure all safety guards and devices are in place.

- Choose the right blade for the job. A sharp tungsten carbide combination blade is good for both crosscutting and ripping without frequent resharpening. For information on blade types and uses, refer to earlier sections of this chapter.

General Procedures

- Follow **Basic Saw Safety** (page 230).

- If you don't have someone to help with long stock, use a roller stand or extension table to support the work.

- Always return the motor head to the column stop.

- When crosscutting or mitring, keep hands at least six inches away from the blade. **Do not adjust length of cut until motor is back at column.**

- Slope the table top back slightly to keep the blade at the column, thereby preventing contact with stock being placed in position.

- Do not allow the blade to cut too quickly when crosscutting or mitring.

- Avoid drawing the blade completely out of the cut. The cut piece, whether large or small, often moves. When the saw is rolled back towards the column, the teeth can grab the piece and shoot it in any direction.

- Do not cut by pushing the saw away from you into the stock. The material can lift up and fly over the fence.

Ripping and Crosscutting

- For regular ripping, turn the motor away from the column to the in-rip position. Feed stock into the saw from the right side.

- To cut wide stock, change the saw to the out-rip position. Feed stock into the saw from the left side. Operators accustomed to in-ripping may find this set-up awkward. Remember—the blade must turn **up and toward** the person feeding the stock.

- Do not force the cut. Allow the blade through the wood at its own pace.

- To avoid kickback, take the following precautions.

  — Maintain proper alignment of blade with fence.
  — Adjust anti-kickback device (*Figure 186*) 1/8 inch below the surface of stock being fed.
  — Use a sharp blade, free of gum deposits and with teeth properly set.

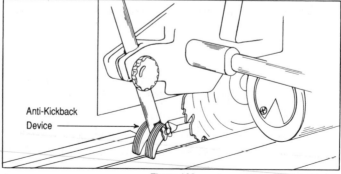

Anti-Kickback Device

Figure 186
Anti-kickback Device

— When binding occurs, stop saw and open kerf with a wedge.
— After completing cut, remove stock from rotating blade to prevent overheating and possible kickback.
— Always push stock all the way through past the blade.
— Do not leave machine with motor running.
— Use a push stick when ripping narrow pieces. Have suitably sized and shaped pushsticks for other jobs as well.

For information on pushsticks and feather boards, see elsewhere in this chapter.

Jigs

The control provided by a well-made jig is essential for making irregular cuts safely and accurately.

Keep the commonly used jigs (*Figure 187*) on hand. Jigs such as these for making stair and doorframe wedges and tapers are designed to carry stock past the blade with the saw locked in the rip position.

Where the saw is drawn into the stock, clamp or nail jigs to the table to prevent slipping.

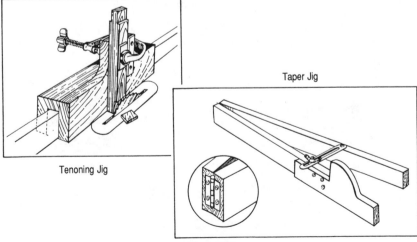

Taper Jig

Tenoning Jig

Figure 187
Jigs

279

Re-sawing with Blade Horizontal

The rip fence on the radial arm saw is too low for supporting material to be re-sawn on edge. Therefore the material must be laid flat on the table and the motor must be turned so the blade is parallel to the table. The closeness of the arbor requires an auxiliary table top and fence to re-saw thin stock.

Because the kickback fence can't be used and controlling stock is sometimes difficult, re-sawing on the radial arm saw can be hazardous.

If no other equipment is available, rip the stock halfway through, then turn it around and complete the cut.

On the second cut, be sure to push the two halves well past the blade once they have been cut apart. Pushsticks and featherboards clamped to the table can reduce hazards.

Dadoes

A dado head is an essential tool for cutting grooves, rabbets, and dadoes. A groove is cut with the grain; a dado is cut across the grain; and a rabbet is a shoulder cut along the edge of a board.

The most common dado head consists of two outside cutters and several inside chippers between the outside cutters (*Figure 188*).

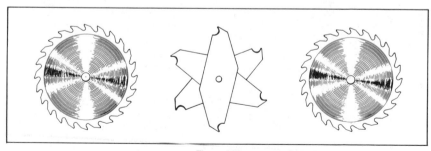

Figure 188
Dado Head Cutter Blades and Chippers

Another type is sometimes called a quick-set dado, consisting of four tapered washers and a blade. By rotating the locking washers, the blade will oscillate and cut a groove to the desired width.

Because of their small size, dado heads do not run at the peripheral feed speed on a big radial arm saw. As a result, the blade feeds itself too fast, either stopping the motor or lifting the work and throwing it back. To prevent this, make several light passes, lowering the dado head 1/8 to 1/4 inch each time.

Dado heads require guards for safety. Always make sure guards are in place before starting work.

Proper rotation of the teeth is **up and toward** you.

Other Accessories

Rotary accessories of various types are advertised as turning the radial arm saw into a multifunction machine. Operators should remember that the saw has its limitations. Possible problems include the following.

- Shaper heads run too slow for safe and smooth work.
- Grinding stones may run too fast or slow and are not recommended.
- Sanding drums tend to run too fast and may burn the wood.

22 POWER TOOLS - AIR

Many different types of tools are powered by compressed air. They are fast, powerful, and ideal for repetitive tasks such as the nailing of large areas of roof decking or chipping and breaking concrete. A compressor, powered by a combustion or electric motor, supplies the air for the tools.

Air powered tools include

— jack hammers
— chipping hammers
— drills
— grinders
— sanders
— staplers
— framing nailers
— wrenches
— brad nailers
— winches
— air nozzles
— saws
— buffers
— impact tools
— sprayers.

· Run combustion engines outside or in a well-ventilated area to prevent the build-up of carbon monoxide gas. Always keep a fire extinguisher near flammable liquids.

· When moving compressors to another location, ask for help or use mechanical devices to prevent back injuries.

· Occasionally workers suffer eye injuries when compressed air is used to blow out formwork. Wear safety goggles and respiratory protection.

· Always secure hose connections with wire or safety clips to prevent the hose from whipping except when automatic cut-off couplers are used.

· Make sure hoses are clear of traffic and pose no tripping hazards.

- Replace worn-out absorption pads and springs. Too much vibration of the tool can damage nerves in fingers, hands, and other body parts. This is called "white finger disease" or Raynaud's Syndrome.

- Some tools have a high decibel rating — for instance, jack hammers and impact drills. To prevent hearing loss, always wear hearing protection.

- Never tamper with safety devices. Keep hands away from discharge area — on nailers in particular.

- Match the speed rating of saw blades, grinding wheels, cut-off wheels, etc. to tool speed. Too fast or too slow a rotation can damage the wheels, release fragments, and injure workers.

- Never use air to blow dust or dirt out of work clothes. Compressed air can enter the skin and bloodstream with disastrous results.

- Turn off the pressure to hoses when the system is not in use.

- Turn off the air pressure when changing pneumatic tools or attachments.

- Never "kink" a hose to stop air flow.

Most air-powered tools need very little maintenance. At the end of the shift, put a teaspoon of oil in the air inlet and run the tool a second or two to protect against rust.

Dust, moist air, and corrosive fumes can damage the equipment. An in-line regulator filter and lubricator will extend tool life.

Before start-up, check the couplings and fittings, blow out the hose to remove moisture and dirt, and clean the nipple before connecting the tool. Set the air pressure according to manufacturer's specifications and open gradually.

Compressed air can be dangerous. Hazards include

- **Air embolism** - This is the most serious hazard, since it can lead to death. If compressed air from a hose or nozzle enters even a tiny cut on the skin, it can form a bubble in the bloodstream — with possibly fatal results.

- **Physical damage** - Compressed air directed at the body can easily cause injuries — including damage to eyes and ear drums.

- **Flying particles** - Compressed air at only 40 pounds per square inch can accelerate debris to well over 70 miles per hour when it is used to blow off dust, metal shavings, or wood chips. These particles then carry enough force to penetrate the skin.

23 POWER TOOLS - EXPLOSIVE

Referred to as *explosive-actuated* or *powder-actuated*, these tools use a powder charge to fire a fastener into hard materials such as concrete, mild steel, and masonry. They provide a fast, efficient means of fastening certain combinations of materials.

Used improperly, powder-actuated tools present obvious hazards. For that reason, most jurisdictions—including Ontario—require that operators be trained before using the tools.

Hazards

Flying Particles - This is the major hazard. On impact, materials may break up, blow apart, or spall off. This often happens when fasteners are fired too close to a corner of masonry or concrete or when they strike material such as glazed tile, hollow tile, or thin marble tile.

Ricochets - These usually result when the tool is not held at right angles to the material or the fastener hits a particularly hard base material such as stone or hardened steel. Always check the base material to ensure that it can safely accept the fastening device.

Noise - Powder-actuated tools create an extreme pulse of sound when fired. Operators and others in the area should wear hearing protection. This is especially important when the tool is operated in a confined space.

Sprains and Strains - These injuries usually result from using the tool repeatedly in awkward, cramped, or unbalanced positions. Operators should try to work from a balanced position on a solid surface.

Explosions - There is always the risk of explosion or fire when the tools are used in atmospheres contaminated by flammable vapour, mist, or dust. The work area must be well-ventilated—mechanically if necessary, as in confined spaces.

Blow-Through - When the base material does not offer enough resistance, the fastener may pass completely through and fly out the other side. This is particularly dangerous when fasteners penetrate walls, floors, or ceilings where other trades may be working. Areas behind and under material, as well as around it, should be checked and kept clear of people if necessary.

Protective Equipment

In addition to the standard personal protective equipment required on construction projects (see Chapter 6), the operator of a powder-actuated tool should wear hearing protection, eye protection, and a face shield. Heavy shirts and pants provide some protection against ricochets and flying fragments of material and fasteners.

Types

High-Velocity - High-velocity powder-actuated tools use the exploding cartridge to propel the fastener directly rather than by a piston. These tools are rarely used in construction, except in special cases to penetrate thick steel or very hard material. These applications are usually military, salvage, or underwater. No one should operate high-velocity tools without special training.

Low-Velocity - Most powder-actuated tools used in construction are low-velocity. The explosive charge drives a piston which in turn drives the fastener.

Many different low-velocity tools are available. Some are specialized for certain trades such as drywalling. Others are fitted with various pistons, base plates, spall stops, and protective shields for heavier-duty work.

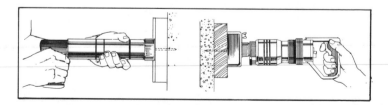

Generally low-velocity tools should only be used on mild or structural grade steels no thicker than 7 mm (1/4").

Studs are fasteners consisting of a smooth shank portion which is driven into the base material and a threaded portion to which a fitting or other object can be attached with a nut.

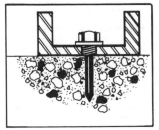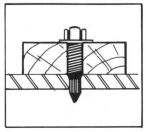

Eye-pin studs allow for items such as wires to be attached through an opening.

Generally pins and studs should not be used on hard, brittle, or glazed materials such as cast iron, marble, tiles, and most stone. The fastener will either fail to penetrate and ricochet or the base material will shatter or spall.

Materials whose hardness or ductility is unknown should be tested first. Try to drive a pin into the material with a normal hammer. If the pin point is blunted or fails to penetrate at least 2 mm (1/16"), a powder-actuated tool should not be used.

Operation

Pistons - Specialized pistons are available for various types of pins and threaded studs. The piston must be suited to the fastener. Some powder-actuated tools may have only one piston to be used with only certain types of pin. Most general-purpose tools can take a variety of pistons in accordance with manufacturer's instructions.

Fastener guides are required for different types of fasteners. Special spall stops or protective shields are required for applications such as fastening sheet metal to masonry or sheet metal to structural steel.

Consult the operating manual or the manufacturer to ensure that the right components are being used for the job.

Fasteners

Fasteners used with explosive-actuated tools are made of special steel to allow them to penetrate materials without breaking or bending.

The fastener is fitted with a tip or eyelet as a guide. This aligns the fastener in the tool as it is being driven. It is also used to retain the fastener in the tool.

Eye Pin   Threaded Stud

There are two basic types of fasteners—pins and studs.

Pins are nut-like fasteners designed to attach one material to another, such as wood to concrete. Head diameters are available between 7 mm (1/4") and 9 mm (3/8"). Washers of various types and diameters are available for different applications. There are also special devices on the pin that can be used to shear through wood, for instance, without splitting it.

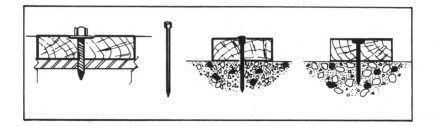

Pins - Pins should be selected for their length and application. As a general rule, pins need not be driven into concrete more than 25 mm (1"). Using a longer pin is generally unnecessary and also requires a stronger cartridge. Follow manufacturers' recommendations on length, penetration, and appropriate material. Testing may be necessary on some masonry materials that vary widely in hardness and durability.

Cartridges - Manufacturers recommend certain cartridges for certain applications. Because recommendations cannot cover every possibility, testing may be required with unfamiliar material. The general rule is to start with the weakest cartridge and increase one load number at a time to reach the penetration required. Too strong a charge may shatter the material or cause ricochets or blow-through.

Standard loads, colour coding, and velocities for cartridges are listed below.

Colour Identification of Powder Load Strengths

Load number	Cartridge case colour	Powder load colour	Nominal velocity	
			m/s	(ft/s)
1	Brass	Grey	91.4	300
2	Brass	Brown	118.8	390
3	Brass	Green	146.3	480
4	Brass	Yellow	173.7	570
5	Brass	Red	201.2	660
6	Brass	Purple	228.6	750
7	Nickel	Grey	256	840
8	Nickel	Brown	283.5	930
9	Nickel	Green	310.9	1020
10	Nickel	Yellow	338.3	1110
11	Nickel	Red	365.8	1200
12	Nickel	Purple	393.2	1290

Fastening Steel

Low-velocity powder-actuated tools should not be used on hardened steels, tool steels, or spring steels. Where the grade of steel is unknown, test by trying to hammer the fastener in. If the pin is blunted, bent, or fails to enter at least 2 mm (1/16"), the tool won't do the job.

Don't try to fire a fastener any closer than 13 mm (1/2") to the free edge of steel. Keep in mind that this applies only to steel. When fastening steel to concrete, you must consider the allowable margin for concrete as well.

When fastening two pieces of thin sheet steel to a base material, hold the sheets together. A gap between them caused by bending may lead to a ricochet

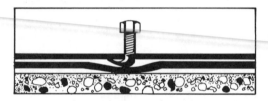

Fastening Concrete and Masonry

Concrete and masonry materials are not always uniform in consistency or hardness. As a result, they may spall, chip, or cause a ricochet when the fastener strikes a spot or layer harder than the rest. Use the spall guard recommended by the manufacturer.

Once material is spalled or left with a ricochet hole, do not fire a second pin any closer than 50 mm (2") to the damaged area. The area may be weakened and spall further or cause a ricochet off its sloped edge.

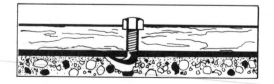

Since pins tend to cause breaks near the free edges of concrete and masonry materials, they should not be driven closer than 63 mm (2 1/2") to a free edge.

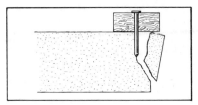

Misfires

Follow the procedures for dealing with misfired cartridges in the operating manual. When this information is not available, take the following steps.

• Hold the tool against the material for at least 00 seconds in case firing is delayed

• Remove the cartridge from the tool with the tool pointed toward soft material such as wood.

• Regulations require that a misfired cartridge be placed in a container of water.

• Keep the misfired cartridge separate from unused cartridges and return it to the manufacturer for disposal. Never throw misfired cartridges in the garbage.

General Safeguards

• Explosive-actuated tools should not be used, handled, or stored carelessly.

• Don't fire fasteners through pre-drilled holes for two reasons:

1) Unless the fastener hits the hole squarely, it will probably shatter the edge.

2) The fastener derives its holding power from compressing the material around it. A pre-drilled hole reduces this pressure and therefore the fastener's holding power.

- Because pressure must be applied to the material into which a fastener is being driven before the tool will fire, working from a ladder is not recommended. For work overhead or at heights, operate the tool from a scaffold or other approved work platform. That helps to ensure a solid, balanced stance.

- Do not leave the tool unattended unless it's locked in a box.

- Load the tool immediately before firing. Don't walk around with the tool loaded.

- Do not use powder-actuated tools in areas where there may be exposure to explosive vapours or gases.

Maintenance

All parts of the tool exposed to detonation gases from the cartridge should be cleaned and lightly oiled in keeping with the manufacturer's instructions. Failure to clean the tool as recommended can lead to corrosion, pitting, fouling, and failure to work properly. Ideally, the tool should be cleaned before being returned to storage.

Storage

Regulations require that both the tool and the cartridges be stored in a locked container with explosive loads of different strengths in separate compartments or containers.

Cartridges should only be removed from the locked container when they are going to be used immediately.

Regulations

- Any worker using an explosive-actuated tool must be instructed in its safe and proper use.

- Before using the tool, the operator must check to ensure that it is in proper working order.

- All tools must have a proper guard at least 75 mm in diameter mounted on the barrel.

- The tool must require two separate actions before it will fire:
  1) pressure against the surface of the material
  2) action of the trigger.

- Explosive-actuated tools must be stored in a locked container when not in use or when left unattended.

- The tool must not be loaded until ready for immediate use. Once loaded, it must not be left unattended.

- The tool must never be pointed at anyone.

- Cartridges must be marked or labelled for easy identification. Cartridges of different strengths must be stored in separate compartments or containers.

- Misfired cartridges must be placed in a container of water and be removed from the project.

24 FORMWORK

In most cases, the formwork required for concrete construction is built by carpenters. Shoring and bracing support the forms that contain in turn the wet concrete. Formwork must also support the temporary weight of material such as bundles of reinforcing steel and live loads of workers and equipment.

General

There are three stages in formwork operations:
— assembly and erection
— concrete placement
— stripping and dismantling.

To be done safely, each of these jobs requires planning, knowledge, and skill from both supervisors and workers. Design and planning are a supervisory function that may also legally require a professional engineer's involvement. Small construction and renovation jobs, however, sometimes call for design on site by workers.

Where design drawings are provided, it is important to construct the formwork as designed. Any confusion regarding the design should be cleared up with the designer.

If site conditions require changes or the design does not seem to suit the situation, clarification should also be obtained from the designer. Formwork failures frequently involve deviations from the original design that were done without consulting the designer. They may also involve human error. For these reasons, formwork and shoring must always be inspected before concrete is placed.

All large formwork installations in Ontario must be designed by a professional engineer. But there are always smaller jobs of moderate height or depth – basements, footings, stairs – that may include formwork designed and constructed on the site.

Every carpenter should therefore know the type of formwork needed and how to build, install, and dismantle it safely.

Formwork must always be constructed according to good, safe and sound carpentry practice. There must be

— adequate braces and supports
— reliable bearing surfaces, especially where wood structures are involved
— adequate ties, bolts, or bracing to prevent movement or bulging.

Because wood is relatively soft, it will crush under heavy loads such as concrete when the bearing surface of joists on stringers or studs on wales is not adequate.

Crushing can be avoided by increasing the bearing area between members, using spreader washers (Figure 189), or increasing the number of joists or studs.

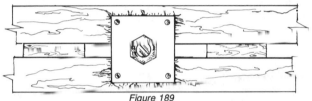

Figure 189
Spreader Washer on Wooden Wale System

Hazards

The following are the main hazard areas in formwork operations.

- **Falls** – The major hazard because they are **potentially fatal**. Cramped work areas, inadequate access, failure to install guardrails, failure to use fall-arrest systems, tools or material left underfoot, surfaces slippery from form oil can all lead to falls. Ladders are also frequently involved in falls.

- **Materials handling – The activity most frequently connected with injury.** Improper or excessive materials handling can result in sprains, strains, and overexertion in shoulders, arms, and back, as well as bruises, abrasions, and crushed fingers.

- **Struck against** – Common because formwork operations are constantly changing and involve the movement of heavy, awkward, and pointed components. Wales, beams, panels, snap-ties, nails, bolts, and rebar can cause punctures, cuts, contusions, and abrasions.

- **Struck by** – Another common cause of injury. Rebar, formwork panels, concrete buckets, and other material hoisted overhead can strike workers. Struck-by injuries can also be caused by hammers, pry bars, stakes, wedges, and material such as joists and panels during stripping.

- **Electrical contact** – Power tools, extension cords, and temporary supply and wiring systems used under less-than-ideal conditions – mud, ground water, wet excavations, fresh concrete – can lead to ground faults, shortcircuits, and shock hazards. Ground fault circuit interrupters are legally required for portable tools used outdoors or in wet locations.

- **Collapses** – Even with advanced methods of design and installation, there is always the risk that formwork, slabforms, wall forms, and other large components can come loose, slip out of place, or fall over, striking or crushing workers underneath.

- **Health hazards** – The spraying of form oils and curing compounds can irritate the lungs. Contact with these chemicals can irritate the skin, leading to redness, inflammation, or dermatitis. The same conditions can result from the abrasive/corrosive effect of skin contact with concrete or cement, especially when inadvertently left inside boots all day.

- **Environmental conditions** – Ice, snow, and rain create slippery conditions. Wind can be a major hazard. Handling sheets of plywood becomes more difficult, panels may require more bracing, and hoisting gets harder, especially with large panels or tables.

- **Dust and concrete** – Blowing dust and flying concrete particles during the chipping or cleaning of formwork can injure unprotected eyes.

- **Access equipment** – Access equipment such as ladders and scaffolds is involved not only in falls but in slips, trips, and other accidents. Hazards include ladders not tied off, workers carrying materials while climbing, ladders obstructed at top or bottom, scaffolds not completely decked in, and scaffolds erected or dismantled without fall protection.

- **Lighting** – Inadequate lighting can create or aggravate hazards when workers install or strip forms in dark areas or place concrete at night.

Injuries

Formwork hazards can lead to the injuries—and be prevented by the measures—described below.

- **Eye injuries** – These are quite prevalent in formwork operations. Most result from particles of wood or concrete that fall or are blown into the eye during chipping and cleaning. The injuries may not be severe but most can be prevented by wearing eye protection. It is strongly recommended that everyone on site wear eye protection at all times.

- **Cuts, scrapes, punctures** – The manhandling necessary to install and strip formwork can lead to cut hands, arms, and legs, as well as pinched or crushed fingers. Gloves help to prevent injuries from rough or sharp edges on formwork components. But workers must also have the knowledge, skill, and physical ability necessary for safe materials handling. That means knowing your limitations and asking for help when needed.

  Formwork involves protruding objects such as nails, snap ties, conduit, and bolts that can leave cuts and punctures. Where possible, these objects should not be left sticking out or should be covered over.

- **Back injuries** – These injuries are frequently related to materials handling. The most important preventive measure is back care. Exercise programs, warm-ups before work, and knowing your limitations can help to prevent sprains and strains. Wherever necessary, get help or use dollies, carts, or other mechanical devices.

- **Ankle sprains and fractures** – Working in close quarters, stepping over debris and material, climbing into excavations, turning with awkward loads, jumping down from scaffolds or benches--these can lead to ankle and other foot or leg injuries. Prevention starts with proper housekeeping and materials handling.

- **Bruises and contusions** – Handling formwork under rushed, cramped, or slippery conditions or beyond your limitations can lead to bruises. Bruises and contusions also result from contact with protruding formwork components.

  More serious are contusions from falling formwork materials. Formwork must be braced to ensure stability, especially under windy conditions. Try to avoid areas where work such as hoisting or stripping is being done overhead.

- **Fall injuries** – All of the injuries above, and many others, can result from falls.

  Most falls are caused by missing or inadequate guardrails, failure to use fall-arrest equipment, failure to completely plank scaffolds and other work platforms, and standing or climbing on surfaces not meant to stand or climb on—for example, the tops of wall forms or 2 x 4 wales.

  Installing and stripping formwork often requires the use of a fall-arrest system.

  > Fall-arrest equipment should be readily available and used whenever workers are exposed to the risk of falling more than 3 metres or falling from any height into dangerous machinery, substances, or objects such as rebar.

  Falls also result from holes left unguarded or uncovered in formwork. These should be covered up or fitted with guardrails as quickly as possible. Where this cannot be done, the area should be roped off and posted with warning signs to prevent unauthorized entry.

Planning

Planning is the first, and most important, step in reducing hazards and preventing injuries.

Because formwork operations must often be carried out in congested areas where other trades are also working, planning is essential in making the most of the time and space available to improve safety and efficiency.

Planning is a must for fall protection, work platforms, material staging areas, housekeeping, and material handling and movement.

Planning should take place at every level from manager through supervisor to worker. Planning labour, materials, equipment, and work schedule to meet design requirements is the responsibility of management and supervision.

Workers must plan the details of their assigned tasks based on the most effective work methods and safety measures to follow in each case.

Design

Safety and economy are the main factors in design. Both have to be considered because adjustments in one affect the other.

For example, reducing the support structure for wall forms in expectation of reduced pouring rates should not be considered if the rate of pour is not going to be controlled on the job.

Fresh concrete exerts a pressure on formwork similar to liquids. However, concrete starts to set when poured so that if the pour rate is slow the maximum pressure can be reduced, since concrete at the bottom will be set before concrete at the top is poured. Similarly, if the forms are filled to the top immediately, they must be able to withstand the pressure of the full liquid head. Liquid concrete exerts a minimum pressure of 150 pounds/foot^2 times the height.

Other factors determine how long concrete will remain liquid, such as temperature, slump, vibration, and admixtures. For example, concrete will set much more quickly in hot summer weather than cold winter weather. As a result, the same form filled at the same pour rate may be subjected to greater pressure in winter than in summer.

Concrete pumping may cause additional pressure, as well as vibration, on forms and must be considered at the design stage. The action of the pump sends surges of pressure through the piping system which are often transmitted directly to the forms, especially for narrow walls or columns. Vibration may move the forms or loosen bracing, ties, or spreaders.

Pressure acts perpendicular to formwork surfaces (Figure 190). This causes an outward thrust for typical wall or column forms. However, it can also cause uplift for battered or sloping forms. These require hold-down anchors or tie-down braces. The anchors will prevent the forms from lifting up or floating on the concrete.

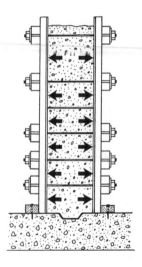
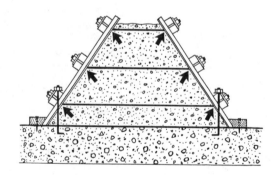

Figure 190
Pressure of Concrete on Vertical and Battered Formwork
(Note expansion anchors holding down battered form.)

Bracing systems and spreaders for wall forms must be considered. Concrete filling the bottom of the form may cause forces at the top to push the two sides together unless they are properly braced and/or separated with spreaders. Formwork has to be designed to resist such forces. Care must also be taken during pouring to ensure that spreaders are not removed until concrete has reached at least two-thirds of the form height.

Where box forms are used – for instance, on one-piece covers for open-cut tunnels – bracing must be provided for the side thrusts caused by uneven pouring rates of the walls. Resisting these forces requires that the system be tied together and securely braced (Figure 191).

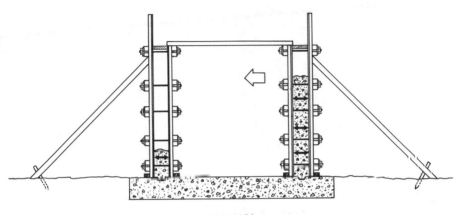

Figure 191
Open-cut tunnel formwork with bracing and spreaders on each side

Formwork should be designed and constructed with stripping and removing as well as pouring in mind. On wooden forms, crush plates or filler strips should be used at corners such as slab-and-column or slab-and-wall intersections (Figure 192). The plates or strips are easily removed with a wrecking bar and, once removed, make the stripping of adjacent panels much easier.

The strips should be big enough to leave space at the edges of the panels to accommodate wrecking bars.

When formwork has to be manhandled during assembly or dismantling, design should ensure that components are manageable. Formwork panels are not only heavy but awkward (Figure 193). Realistic design demands consideration of size as well as weight of panels.

A formwork panel or wall form to be lifted as a single unit must be designed to withstand the loads and forces exerted by hoisting (Figure 194). In most cases this means designing a more substantial structure. Fastening components may also need more attention at the

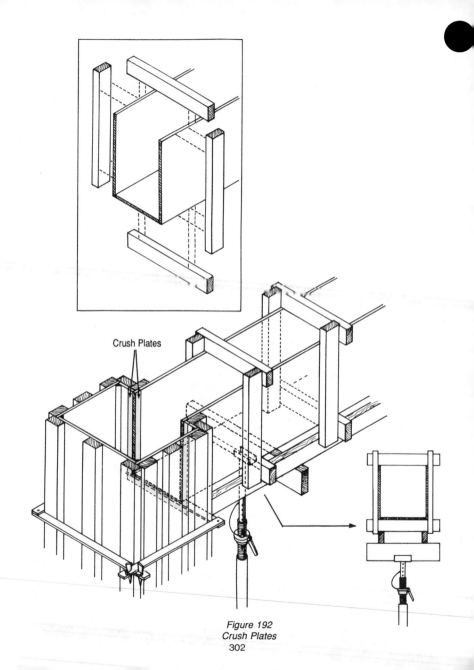

Crush Plates

Figure 192
Crush Plates
302

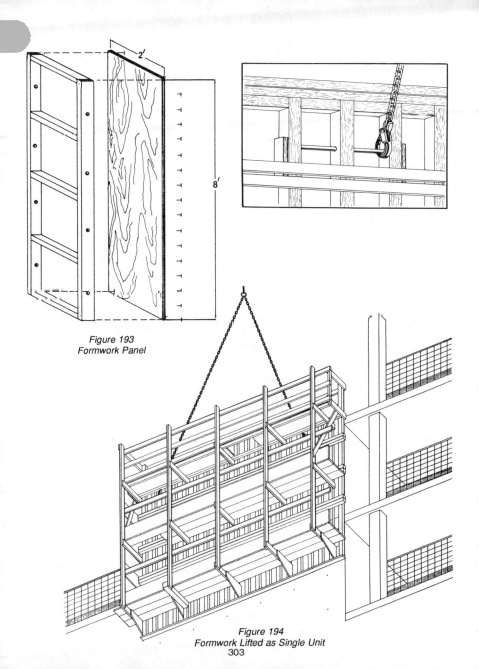

Figure 193
Formwork Panel

Figure 194
Formwork Lifted as Single Unit

303

design stage. For example, simple nailing may not be enough to hold plywood sheets.

Special attention must also be applied to the design, construction, and use of pick points for hoisting. The strongbacks and wales must be securely attached to the formwork. The pick points must be located so that the panel hangs properly during installation, concrete placement, and removal.

Types of Formwork

Below Grade

The first concern with formwork below grade is the stability of the excavation walls. Walls must be either shored or sloped according to soil type as defined by the Regulations for Construction Projects. Figure 195 shows typical slopes.

In most cases the shoring must be designed by an engineer. Engineers may also specify slopes for excavations. In both instances the design drawings must be kept on the project.

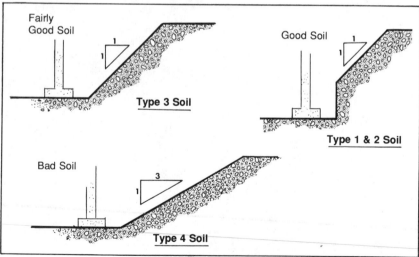

Figure 195
Excavation Slopes for Good, Fairly Good, and Poor Soil

Excavations should be kept essentially dry. Water should be pumped out. Mud should be cleared off and replaced by compacted granular material in work areas and on surfaces where concrete will be placed. Mud presents slipping hazards and can lead to inferior construction if not removed or replaced.

Since mud has to be removed before concrete is placed, it might as well be removed before formwork is constructed and thereby reduce slipping hazards at both stages.

Water and mud also contribute to electrical hazards. Grounding and insulation must be effective and intact. Ground fault circuit interrupters (GFCIs) are required by law on all portable tools used outdoors or in wet locations.

Formwork for footings and grade walls frequently begins before excavation in the area is complete. Trucks and excavating equipment put workers on foot at the risk of being struck down or run over.

Wherever possible, formwork operations should be roped off from other work such as excavation or pile-driving (Figure 196). Separate access ramps for vehicles and workers are strongly recommended. Stairs are an even better alternative for personnel on foot.

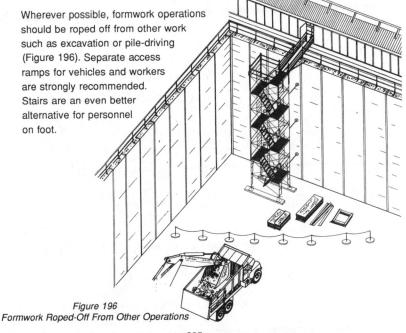

Figure 196
Formwork Roped-Off From Other Operations

Mud sills must be used to support any shoring or bracing that rests on soil in the excavation (Figure 197). The sill must bear on the soil throughout its length. Sills should not be used to bridge holes or irregular surfaces. To ensure uniform bearing, soil should be levelled before sills are set in position.

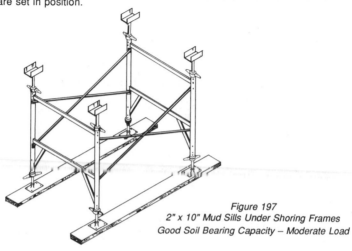

Figure 197
2" x 10" Mud Sills Under Shoring Frames
Good Soil Bearing Capacity – Moderate Load

The soil must have the capacity to bear whatever loads are applied. This information may or may not be on the design drawings.

In Situ Bearing Pressures for Dry Soil Conditions (Conservative Estimates)	
Silt and clay	1200lbs/ft^2
Sands	4000lbs/ft^2
Gravelly sands	6000lbs/ft^2
Gravel	8000lbs/ft^2

Soil that supports bracing or shoring should be compacted and qualify as good soil at least (cohesive, hard, with no water). Professional advice is recommended and may be required for heavy structures such as elevated equipment supports shored at or below grade.

Formwork in these situations is frequently built in place. Planning is required to store material and equipment out of the way, dispose of scrap and debris, and ensure safe, efficient access (Figure 198). Because conditions are often cramped and scrap accumulates quickly, it is important to clean up as work proceeds.

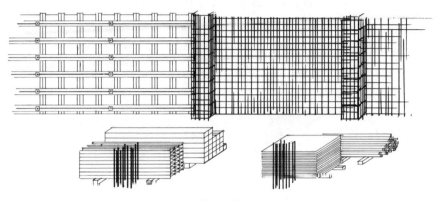

Figure 198
Well-Planned Storage, Access, and Setup

Wall Forms

Wall forms built in place are hazardous to construct. Hazards include
- dowels sticking up from concrete slabs or footings
- unstable work surfaces and access created by poor planning
- manual handling of heavy material such as plywood sheets, panels, wales, and buckets of snap-ties, wedges, and plates
- slippery surfaces at and below grade
- inadequate design
- improper construction.

The best protection against dowels is a wood cover built of lumber at least 1 1/2 inches thick and wired in place (Figure 199).

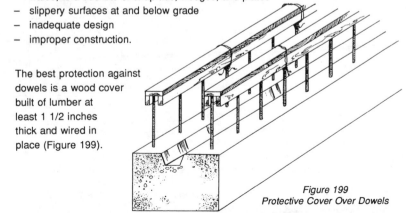

Figure 199
Protective Cover Over Dowels

Starting the Form

Setting up the first form is always hard, heavy, manual work. It calls for enough workers to do the job without overexertion or injury.

Temporary bracing (Figure 200) is needed from the start and at every step to prevent wind loads from toppling the forms – historically the cause of many serious injuries. A wind of 30 km/h will create a dangerous wind load on formwork.

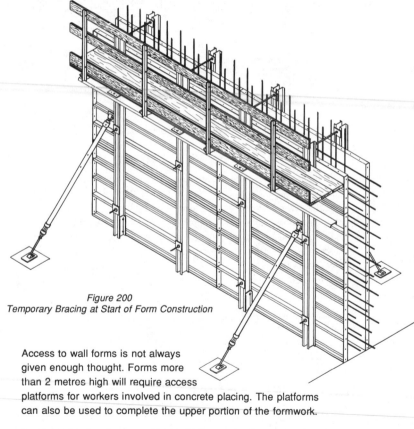

Figure 200
Temporary Bracing at Start of Form Construction

Access to wall forms is not always given enough thought. Forms more than 2 metres high will require access platforms for workers involved in concrete placing. The platforms can also be used to complete the upper portion of the formwork.

An alternative is a frame scaffold, which can also be used to install reinforcing steel (Figure 201).

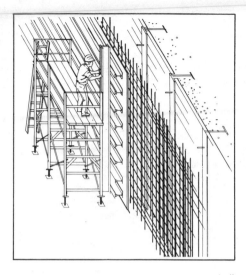

Figure 201
Scaffolding for Access

Fall-arrest systems or scaffolds with guardrails must be used where workers may fall more than 3 metres (10 feet) or onto hazards such as projecting dowels (Figure 202)

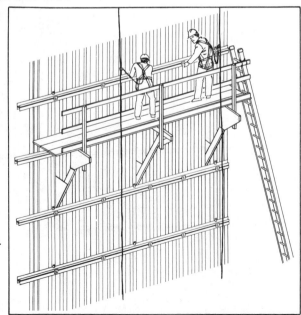

Figure 202
Worker wears fall-arrest while
attaching wales to threaded rods.

Materials should be distributed along the work location to minimize further handling. But traffic and work areas must be kept clear for the safe movement and installation of material.

Form Construction

Wall forms must be constructed as designed. The design must indicate clearly what is required.

Some wall forms are designed for specific concrete placement rates expressed in metres of height per hour (m/hr). A wall form in which concrete is placed to a height of one metre in one hour would have a placement rate of 1 m/hr. Slower pouring rates result in lower formwork pressure because the bottom concrete has started to set.

Ensure that ties and braces are installed where indicated on design drawings. Ties should be snugged up. Braces should be securely fastened to forms and wedged or fastened to a support that will not settle or deform under load (Figure 203).

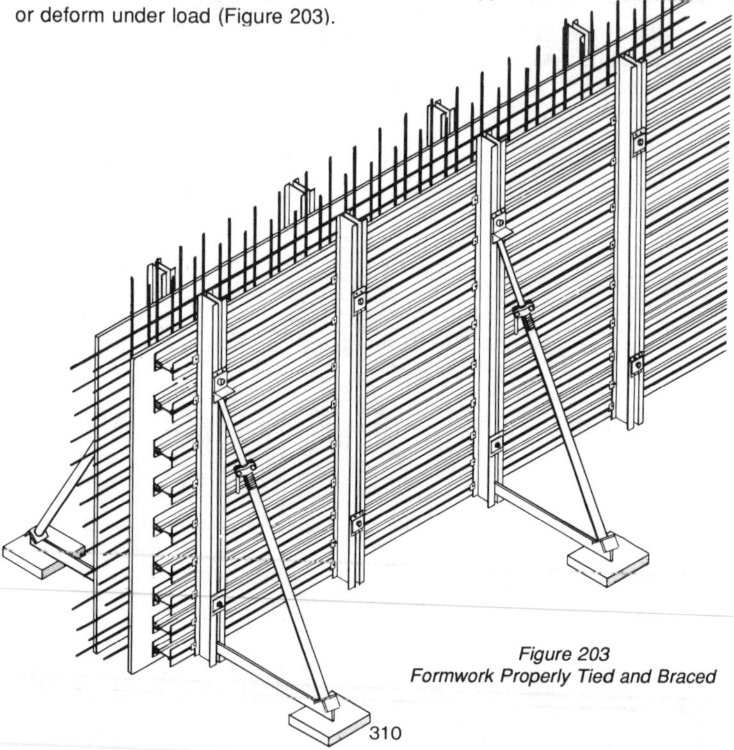

Figure 203
Formwork Properly Tied and Braced

Formwork platforms must be

- capable of bearing at least 50 pounds/foot^2
- adequately supported
- equipped with guardrails
- secured at the level or levels where work such as pouring and stripping will be done.

Recommended design pressures for various pour rates and environmental conditions are set out in CSA Standard S269.3 *Concrete Formwork*. The standard defines a number of other design considerations and should be consulted by field staff.

Slab Forms or Falsework Built in Place

With slab forms built in place the major hazard is falls. Injuries are also connected with the manual handling of heavy materials and components.

Forms built in place usually have to be taken down in place. This should be considered at the construction stage. Stability may also be a consideration where the structure is high, carries heavy loads, and is placed on grade as in bridge and overpass construction.

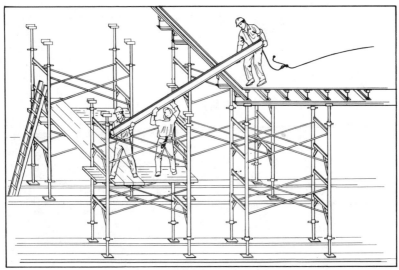

Figure 204
Workers tie off to shoring frames while placing stringers.

Fall protection is difficult to provide for workers building slab forms in place. That's why planning is essential in the design and erection procedure.

Workers should wear a safety belt with the lanyard tied off to the structure of the formwork (Figure 204) This means tying off to the support structure where shoring frame structures are being constructed, tying off to a lifeline when placing plywood panels at a leading edge constructing a guardrail at the edge of the formwork, or tying off to the support structure when tying it together with tube and clamp. Note that this operation should proceed as the structure is being erected and not left until it is all finished.

Wherever possible, cranes or other equipment should be used to move material, thereby reducing the amount of manual carrying, lifting, and handling.

Shoring towers require special consideration.

- Towers must remain stable during construction and dismantling. Guys may be necessary to maintain stability (Figure 205).

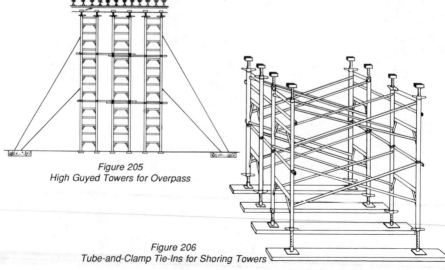

Figure 205
High Guyed Towers for Overpass

Figure 206
Tube-and-Clamp Tie-Ins for Shoring Towers

- If towers are to be tied together and braced horizontally, this should be done as work progresses (Figure 206).

- Shoring towers and shores should be installed so they are plumb to within 1/8 inch in 3 feet.

- Shoring towers should be squared off horizontally.

- Shoring should be snugged up under the stringers with adjustable base plates and U-heads (Figure 207).

Replace this frame.

Figure 207
Typical Shoring Tower with Stringers,
Adjustable Base Plates, and U-Heads

Figure 208
Frame Bent Out of Shape

- If frames do not ride tightly on top of one another after tightening, one or more are out of square and should be replaced (Figure 208).

- With single-post shores, provide adequate lateral bracing (Figure 209). Stairwells and balconies are situations where horizontal bracing for single-post shoring systems may be required.

313

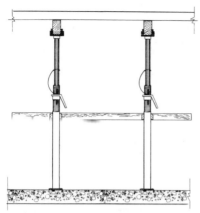

Figure 209
Single-Post Shores with Lateral Bracing

Frequently supports for built-in-place forms are deliberately left out to allow other work to be done. One example might be a row of single-post shores left out until work below is complete (Figure 210). Conversely an area might be supported temporarily during construction by a few single-post shores that will be replaced later by a shoring tower.

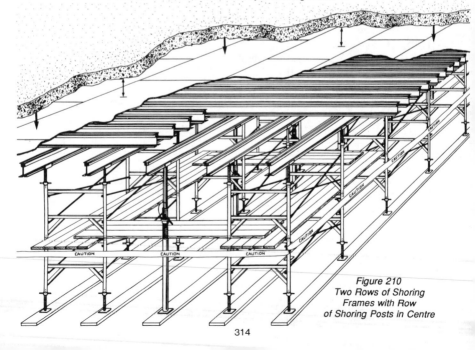

Figure 210
Two Rows of Shoring
Frames with Row
of Shoring Posts in Centre

In these and other instances of incomplete formwork, heavy temporary loads such as bundles of rebar or stacks of plywood should not be placed on the structure. Even on completed formwork, make sure that landed material will not overload the structure.

Flying Forms

Flying forms must always be designed by a professional engineer and constructed, hoisted, moved, and set strictly according to the instructions of the designer or manufacturer.

Using forms designed for typical floors in non-typical situations has resulted in serious accidents. Before using any flying form under non-typical conditions, consult the designer or manufacturer. Wall forms should not be extended in height or width, for instance, or slab panels cantilevered without professional consultation. Such situations usually occur with penthouses or mechanical rooms where wall and ceiling heights are greater than for typical floors.

Apart from misuse, hazards with flying forms include
- stability during initial fabrication
- fill-in work between slab panels
- stripping, flying, and re-setting.

In the last category especially, falls are a common hazard. For fall protection, see the next section.

Although a flying form is designed to be stable when complete, it may not be stable during fabrication or erection. Temporary bracing or temporary support by a crane may be necessary to ensure stability during certain phases of the operation (Figure 211).

One example is setting up trusses for a flying slab formwork table. The trusses must be held upright to be connected or disconnected. If not adequately supported, they can fall over on workers. Trusses and wall panels have also been blown over by wind during fabrication and dismantling.

Work with flying forms requires adequate space for stacking materials and components. Working in cramped quarters is not only difficult but hazardous.

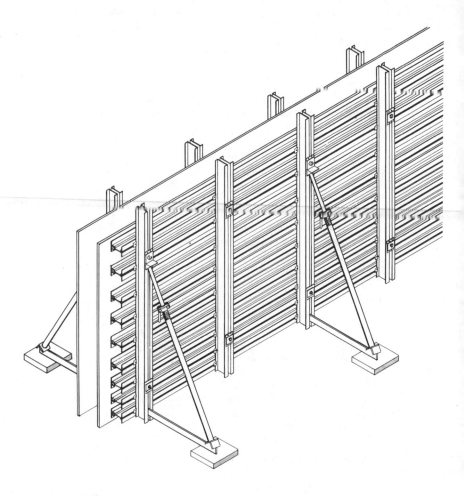

Figure 211
Temporary Support of Shoring System for Flying Wall Form

Fall Protection - Flying Forms

A fall-arrest system should be used by any worker who is
- installing or removing exterior guardrails
- pushing a panel out toward the slab edge
- receiving a panel in from the slab edge
- helping other workers attach rigging hardware such as slings (Figure 212)
- getting on and off and bolting and unbolting wall forms for exterior walls and elevator shafts (Figure 213)
- stepping onto a panel to attach slings to pick points (Figure 214).

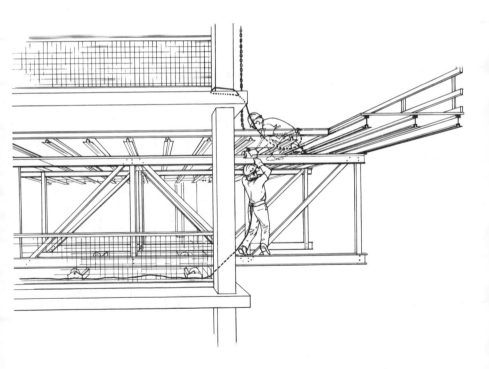

Figure 212
Helping Worker Above

317

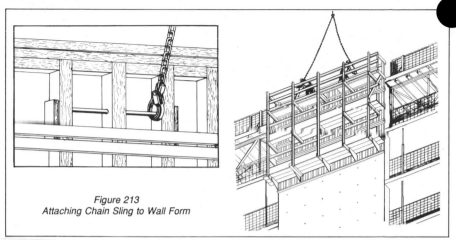

Figure 213
Attaching Chain Sling to Wall Form

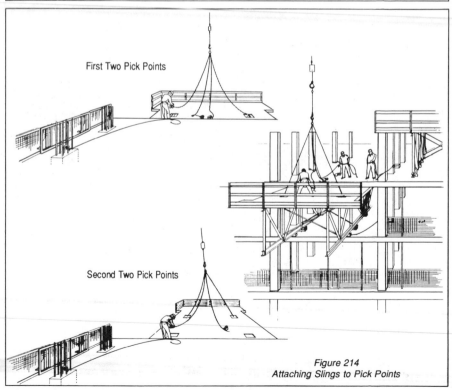

First Two Pick Points

Second Two Pick Points

Figure 214
Attaching Slings to Pick Points

Each worker's fall-arrest system must be attached to an individual anchor independent of the flying form. Contractors can provide for anchorage by casting rebar anchors in columns or other areas to be covered over or filled in later (Figure 215).

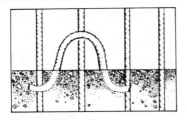

Figure 215
Rebar Anchor Cast in Concrete

Safety Below Flying Forms

The previous section covered the safety of workers flying the forms. But precautions must also be taken to protect workers below the hoisting operation and the public at large, since forms are often swung out over sidewalks and streets. The most efficient protection for workers is to rope off the area below to prevent anyone from entering the area. Pedestrian traffic on sidewalks, and vehicle traffic if necessary, should be detoured around the area while hoisting is under way.

Communication

Flying forms are heavy, large, and awkward. To hoist and move them safely requires clear reliable communication. While hand signals are often necessary, direct radio communication between work crew and crane operator is more accurate and effective. Relying on hand signals alone is not recommended.

Stripping

General

Formwork stripping is probably the most hazardous operation in concrete construction. Hazards include
- falling material
- material and equipment underfoot
- manual handling of heavy or awkward forms, panels, and other components

- prying forms loose from concrete at risk of overexertion, lost balance, and slips and falls.

Hazards can be reduced by
- planning and providing for stripping in the design and construction of formwork
- supplying facilities and equipment for removing materials as they are stripped
- providing proper tools and adequate access for the stripping crew
- training personnel properly for this and other aspects of formwork.

At the design stage, crush plates or filler strips can be specified to facilitate removal at difficult intersections of columns, beams, and wall forms. Later, form oils should be used liberally to make stripping easier.

Wherever possible, materials and debris should be removed from the area as work proceeds. This will reduce the need to walk over or work around things left on floor or ground.

Providing carts or cradles can help the crew remove material and reduce the need for lifting and carrying. Material on a cart can be rolled away. Material in cradles can be hoisted off by a crane.

Climbing partially stripped formwork is not only hazardous but unnecessary. Safe access such as rolling scaffolds or powered elevating work platforms should be provided for stripping formwork at elevated locations.

Poor lighting is sometimes a hazard in formwork stripping. Mobile light stands are probably the best solution, since pigtail stringers can easily be knocked down and damaged during stripping.

Wherever possible, stripping crews should be small. This is especially important with knock-down systems. In small crews each person can keep track of what the others are doing. Workers are not as likely to cause problems for each other. Crews of two or three are recommended for knock-down systems. If more workers are required, they can still be divided into small crews working in separate areas.

Other trades and operations should not be allowed in areas where stripping is under way. Given the many hazards involved, the area should be roped off and warning signs posted.

Knock-Down Slab Systems

Stripping these forms is difficult because much of the work is overhead. The usual arrangement involves shoring frames or a combination of shoring frames and jacks.

Wherever possible, the work should proceed from one side. That means taking out one row of formwork supported by a row of stringers on shoring frames.

The first step is to back off the adjustable base plates and U-heads in one area, which will in turn lower the stringers, joists, and sheathing (Figure 216).

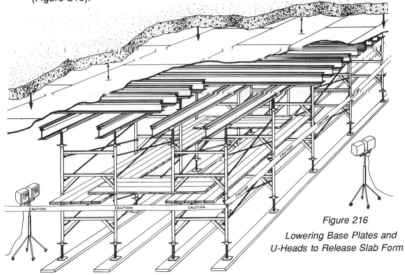

Figure 216
Lowering Base Plates and
U-Heads to Release Slab Form

In practice, however, the sheathing will stick, especially around beams, column caps, and similar points. Wherever possible, stuck sheets should be loosened and removed before the shoring structure is dismantled.

Stripping should proceed in reverse order to erection. Plywood sheathing should be removed first, followed by joists and stringers. The last items to be removed are the shoring frames.

When scaffold or shoring frames are used for access, the platform should be completely decked in with planks (Figure 217). Otherwise

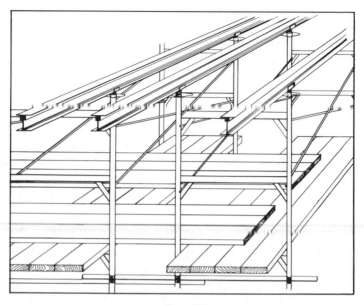

Figure 217
Shoring Frame Fully Planked for Access

planks can shift and slide as workers pry or pull at stuck pieces of
formwork, lose their balance, and fall. This has been a frequent cause of
injuries.

The area where stripping starts should allow access for taking away
material as it is dismantled.

Sound training, well-designed forms, safe access facilities, and
immediate and continuing cleanup can help reduce hazards in stripping
knock-down slab forms.

Built-in-Place Wall Forms

These forms are frequently of only moderate height. Taller types usually
make use of large panels erected and removed by crane rather than
hand.

Built-in-place wall forms are usually a stud-and-wale system using some type of ties.

Where workers cannot reach the top of the wall, scaffolding should be provided for removing wales on the upper level (Figure 218). Safe access is essential for the dismantling and manhandling of wales that are frequently long, heavy, and waterlogged.

Material should then be removed immediately to a staging area.

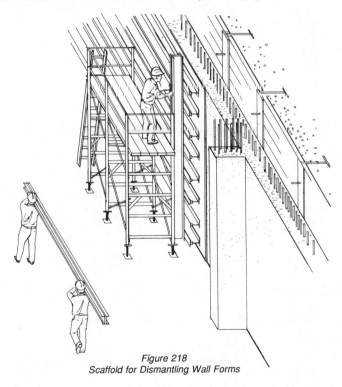

Figure 218
Scaffold for Dismantling Wall Forms

Inspection

Before concrete placing is started, formwork must be inspected by the designer or a competent person to ensure that it has been constructed to provide for worker safety and to meet job specifications.

323

In Ontario, formwork requiring design by an engineer must be inspected by an engineer or a designated competent worker. The worker does not have to be an engineer.

A report must be filed stating whether the formwork has been constructed according to the design. Any discrepancies should be cleared up with the design engineer before concrete placing proceeds.

Regardless of the specific responsibility, it is in everyone's best interest to ensure that the formwork has been inspected by a competent person for workmanship, stability, and conformance with design drawings and specifications.

Inspection should start when the forms are being constructed and continue until concrete placing is complete.

Checking line and grade is best carried out while the formwork is being constructed. Shoring structures should be within the alignment limits specified on the design drawings. Line and grade should also be checked during the pour to determine whether formwork is shifting or deflecting.

Dimensions of special features like beams, column capitals, and inserts are best checked during construction. If inspection is delayed until formwork is completed, some details may be covered up or become more difficult to check.

Columns

Check that
- the proper size and type of materials are used
- column ties or column clamps are spaced according to design drawings
- the spacing of ties or clamps is based on a sound assessment of concrete pressure (generally columns are designed for a full liquid head of 150 pounds/foot^2 times height)
- columns are adequately braced where they are not tied in to a slab form structure.

NOTE   For more information on column formwork pressures, refer to CSA Standard S269.3 *Concrete Formwork* or ACI SP4 *Formwork for Concrete*.

Wall Forms

Check that
- materials and any manufactured components are as specified in design drawings (size and spacing of studs, wales, and ties are crucial to safety)
- ties are snugged up before concrete is placed
- wedges in wedged systems are tight
- nuts in threaded systems are tight
- bracing conforms to design drawings
- free-standing formwork is braced to ensure stability and resistance to loads during concrete placing
- specified pour rates are not exceeded (wall forms are often designed for specific pour rates; exceeding these rates can cause failure or collapse).

Slab Forms

From a safety perspective, this is the most critical type of formwork. The collapse of slab forms has caused many injuries and deaths, whether from flawed design, unauthorized modifications in the field, or failure to inspect.

Proper inspection demands knowledge, experience, and the ability to
1) distinguish between similar but different materials and shoring equipment
2) read and interpret design drawings
3) identify and clear up with the designer any apparent or real discrepancies in components such as shoring frames.

Check that
- grade beams or mud sills supporting shoring are properly sized and located
- hazardous soil conditions such as excessive moisture, freezing, and uncompacted soil are reported and discussed with the designer
- shoring frames and jacks are located and aligned within tolerances specified on the drawings

- shoring frames and jacks are out of plumb no more than 1/8 inch in 3 feet
- adjustable base plates for shoring frames and jacks are snugged up
- U-heads are wedged in place
- stringers are the specified size and number, with supports properly spaced
- aluminum stringers have no bent flanges or other damage
- joists are the specified size and properly spaced
- support structures and shoring for beam bottoms and column capitals are constructed according to design
- lateral bracing is provided where required (for instance, on free-standing formwork for bridges and overpasses)
- the bearing surface for lateral bracing is adequate, that is, stable footings or well-compacted soil
- temporary loads such as rebar are not obviously overloading the system.

Concrete Placing

Inspection of forms should continue during concrete placing. Any signs of movement, crushing, or deflection are cause for alarm. Pouring should be suspended until the situation is corrected.

Watch for the following warning signs:
- movement of single-post shoring for slab forms
- movement or deflection of lateral bracing for single-post shores
- movement of stringers on U-heads
- crushing of wooden stringers on U-heads (Figure 219)

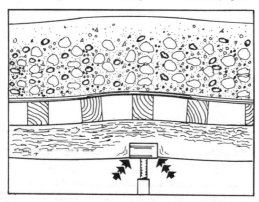

Figure 219
Crushing of Stringer Over U-Head

- shoring that is not snugged up under stringers
- deflection of stringers between supports (Figure 220)

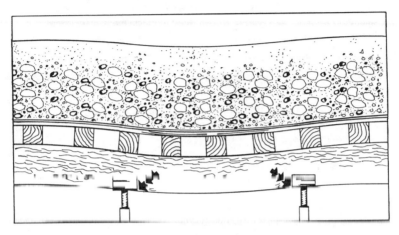

Figure 220
Deflection of Stringers Between Supports

- deflection of wales or strongbacks on wall forms
- bulging of wall forms
- crushing of wales or strongbacks at washers for ties
- movement of wall forms
- uplifting of battered forms
- pour rates that exceed design specifications.

25 WELDING AND CUTTING

Workers using welding and flame-cutting equipment should be trained in safe procedures. That includes proper use of protective equipment and the correct storage, handling, and use of fuel cylinders and welding machines.

Storage and Care of Equipment

- The contents of fuel gas and oxygen cylinders are under high pressure. Never strike, roll, or expose cylinders to extreme heat. Extreme heat can cause fire and explosion.

- Store and secure cylinders upright at all times.

- Keep protective caps in place over valve assemblies. Cylinders containing different gases should be stored separately and isolated from other flammables such as gasoline, solvents, oil, and lumber.

- Coil and hang up loose hoses when not in use to keep them clean and free from contamination and the risk of puncture. If a hose breaks or is punctured, repair it only with a proper coupler. Makeshift repairs with copper tubing can be dangerous because copper reacts with acetylene gas.

- Run hoses through a piece of pipe or between blanks to protect them from traffic.

- Cutting and welding torches are made of soft metal. Never drag the torch by the hose.

- Keep torch tips clean of grease, oil, and slag. Clogged torch tips should be cleaned with suitable cleaning wires, drills, or other devices designed for the purpose.

- Store equipment in a safe place, preferably in a box made for torch parts, hose, and regulators.

- Always use proper fitting wrenches when making connections. **Do not use vise grips or pipe wrenches.**

- For safety, install a **reverse flow check valve** to prevent dangerous flashbacks.

- Cylinders in use should be secured upright or in a rack designed to hold them (Figure 221).

- Do not locate cylinders where they can become part of an electrical circuit. Do not strike electrodes against a cylinder to strike an arc.

- All portable welding equipment must be properly grounded.

- Do not use valve protection caps for lifting or hoisting. Lift cylinders in a secure cradle or basket. Do not transport or hoist by magnets or choker slings.

- Do not use bars under valves or valve protection caps to pry cylinders loose from frozen ground.

- When handling a leaking propane cylinder, remember that your clothing can be saturated with propane and you can draw a trail of gas behind you. Stay away from all ignition sources.

- Like propane, natural gas must be handled with caution because of its flammable and explosive properties.

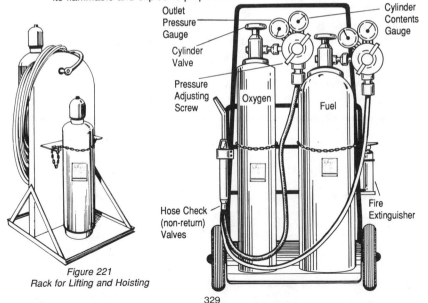

Figure 221
Rack for Lifting and Hoisting

Preparing the Torch

- Make sure that all equipment is working properly before use.

- Inspect valve openings or cylinders to make sure they are clean.

- Crack the cylinder valves by opening one-quarter turn to blow out any impurities before attaching regulators. Close valves.

- Regulator assemblies are fragile. Treat them carefully. Avoid damage to threads by storing assemblies in a case when not in use. Avoid contamination by oil, grease, and dirt.

> **CAUTION** Some propane regulators are interchangeable with acetylene regulators. Propane regulators are usually set for 50 psi while acetylene regulators operate at 5 psi. Using a propane regulator on an acetylene cylinder without adjusting the operating pressure can cause serious flashback. Check the setting on the dial before using.

- Attach the regulator with a wrench. Don't overtighten. Oxygen cylinders have a right-hand thread (clockwise). Fuel gas cylinders have a left-hand thread (counterclockwise).

- Avoid cross-threading or damaging brass parts. Make sure threaded parts are clean before attaching to cylinders.

- After attaching regulators, turn adjusting handle on the regulators counterclockwise to release pressure on the diaphragm spring.

- Attach welding or cutting tip as required.

> **CAUTION** Always stand to the side of the regulator when slowly opening the cylinder valve. Regulators have been known to explode, causing serious injury.

- Open oxygen valve all the way.

- Open propane valve all the way.

- Open acetylene valve half turn only.

- Adjust regulator screws to show slight pressure. After purging the system, shut off the torch valves.

- Check manufacturer's chart for proper regulator setting suited to the tip size and job application. Adjust regulator screw to the required pressure.

Using the Torch

- Wear protective tinted glasses, leather gloves, full-length work pants, and a shirt with sleeves.

- Slowly open the fuel valve on the torch, one-half to one turn, but not all the way. For propane, however, the valve has to be open all the way to prevent frost build-up

- Never use the oxygen hose to blow off clothing. This is a dangerous practice. Oxygen will impregnate clothing and make it highly flammable. A spark can turn you into an instant torch.

- Use caution when cutting or welding near flammable materials. Remember that sparks can carry up to 40 feet.

A fire watch may be required when working near highly flammable materials. Cutting or burning near newly oiled formwork can trigger fires.

- Never burn directly on a concrete floor. The heat from the torch can cause the concrete to expand and shatter with great force. Put a piece of plate between your work and the floor or, better still, work on a welding bench.

- Make sure the torch is pointed away from you and your fellow workers at all times.

- A 4A40BC fire extinguisher must be available wherever oxyacetylene cutting, welding, soldering, or brazing is done. Keep a bucket of water near the work for cooling.

- When using an oxyacetylene cutting torch, workers must wear leather gauntlet gloves and goggles with No. 4 or 5 lens shade.

LENS SHADE SELECTION GUIDE FOR WELDING

Shade numbers are given as a guide only and may be varied to suit individual needs.

Operation	Electrode Size mm (32nd in.)	Arc Current (Amperes)	Minimum Protective Shade	Suggested[1] Shade No. (Comfort)
Shielded Metal Arc Welding (SMAW)	less than 2.5 (3)	less than 60	7	—
	2.5–4 (3–5)	60–160	8	10
	4–6.4 (5–8)	>160–250	10	12
	more than 6.4 (8)	>250–550	11	14
Gas Metal Arc Welding and Flux Cored (GMAW)		less than 60	7	—
		60–160	10	11
		>160–250	10	12
		>250–500	10	14
Gas Tungsten Arc Welding (GTAW)		less than 50	8	10
		50–150	8	12
		>150–500	10	14
Air Carbon (light) Arc Cutting (heavy)		less than 500	10	12
		500–1000	11	14
Plasma Arc Welding (PAW)		less than 20	6	6 to 8
		20–100	8	10
		>100–400	10	12
		>400–800	11	14

Operation	Plate Thickness (mm)	Plate Thickness (in.)	Shade number
Plasma Arc Cutting (PAC)[2]			
Light	less than 300	8	9
Medium	300–400	9	12
Heavy	>400–800	10	14
Torch Brazing (TB)	—	—	3 or 4
Torch Soldering (TS)	—	—	2
Carbon Arc Welding (CAW)	—	—	14
Gas Welding (GW)			
Light	under 3.2	under 1/8	4 or 5
Medium	3.2 to 13	1/8 to 1/2	5 or 6
Heavy	over 13	over 1/2	6 to 8
Oxygen Cutting (OC)			
Light	under 25	under 1	3 or 4
Medium	25 to 150	1 to 6	4 or 5
Heavy	over 150	over 6	5 or 6

1. Shade numbers are given as a rule of thumb. It is recommended to begin with a shade that is too dark to see the weld zone. Then one should go to a lighter shade which gives sufficient view of the weld zone without going below the minimum. In gas welding or oxygen cutting where the torch produces a high yellow light, it is desirable to use a filter lens that absorbs the yellow or sodium line in the visible light of the operation (spectrum).

2. These values apply where the actual arc is clearly seen. Experience has shown that light filters may be used when the arc is hidden by the workpiece.

Reproduced with the permission of the American Welding Society.

©1989 by American Welding Society, 550 N.W. LeJeune Road, P.O. Box 351040, Miami, Florida 33135.   ANSI/AWS F2.2-89

- Workers doing oxyacetylene work should not carry butane lighters.

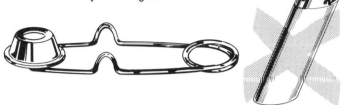

- When using a torch in a confined area, make sure that there is adequate ventilation and a ready exit. Never leave a torch in a confined area with the system under pressure. Fuel gas and oxygen may leak to create a lethal hazard.

- Oxygen and fuel are heavier than air and will collect in low confined areas creating a potential for fire and explosion.

- Pure oxygen under pressure can cause spontaneous combustion in contact with grease and oil. Do not bring these substances together.

> Any escaping gas will displace breathable air in a confined area and create the potential for asphyxiation.

- Should you need to leave the workstation, take the torch with you outside the confined area.

- When shutting off a torch, always close the oxygen valve first and the fuel valve last.

Dismantling the Torch

- Close the cylinder valves.
- Open the torch valves one at a time.
- Release pressure on the regulator diaphragms by turning the adjusting handle counterclockwise.
- Remove regulators, torch, and hoses to a safe storage area.
- Replace cylinder caps to protect valves.

Electric Arc Welding

Safety-minded workers should take nothing for granted when setting up or when the arc is struck and work is under way.

- Know the equipment and make sure that it works properly.

- The welding machine should be in a location free of puddles or wet ground, with cables in good condition and properly connected. Protect cables from traffic.

- Periodic inspections of equipment for loose or corroded connections, damaged cables, and loose or defective jaws on electrode holders and ground clamps will ensure safety.

> **CAUTION**   Always wear a helmet with No. 10, 12, or 14 shade filter lenses depending on type of welding. Never wear tinted cutting goggles for arc welding.

- Ultraviolet rays can burn skin and cause arc eyes. Skin exposed for even short periods of time will develop a burn. Repeated exposure can result in dermatitis (skin inflammation). It is extremely important to prevent exposure by wearing protective gear such as CSA-certified gloves, cuffless trousers, and flash goggles under helmets and face shields.

- Wear safety glasses when chipping slag.

- To protect nearby workers, erect screens and shielding.

The arc welding lens assembly consists of 3 parts. The outside lens is clear plastic or tempered glass. It protects the shade lens from damage. The centre lens is a shade lens which filters out the harmful light. The inner lens is clear and must be plastic.

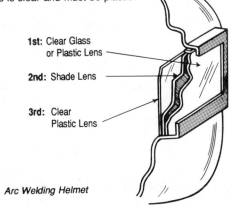

1st: Clear Glass or Plastic Lens

2nd: Shade Lens

3rd: Clear Plastic Lens

Arc Welding Helmet

- Provide adequate ventilation to prevent the accumulation of hazardous fumes from welding and also from gasoline-powered equipment. Fume extractors (Figure 222) and/or respiratory equipment may be required.

- Handle electrode holder, cable connections, and cable carefully to protect insulation and prevent short circuits.

- Remove electrodes from holder when not in use.

- Never ground to other machines or equipment, electrical circuits, or pipes containing gas or flammable liquids.

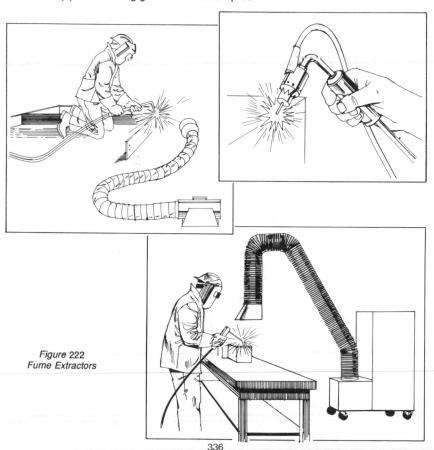

Figure 222
Fume Extractors

26 FLOORING TOOLS AND PRACTICES

Workers in the carpet and resilient floor trade suffer common repeated injuries and related problems. There are five main areas of injury

— back
— knee
— respiratory
— injuries from power tools
— injuries from hand tools.

Most of these injuries can be minimized by planning and the proper choice, use, and maintenance of tools.

Protective Equipment

See Chapter 0 PERSONAL PROTECTIVE EQUIPMENT for equipment required or recommended in construction.

A light type of workshoe may be used instead of a workboot, provided it conforms with the CSA standard for construction.

First aid kits are required on all construction sites. Specific kit contents vary according to the size of the project. For full details, refer to WCB Regulation 950.

Knee Protection

It is essential to protect the knees against long-term injuries from kneeling and working on hard and uneven surfaces.

Rubber knee pads may cause water on the knee, ingrown hair, or other problems. Leather and felt knee protectors help to prevent these problems.

Skin Protection

While working with epoxies, toluene, seam sealers, and other solvents and adhesives, wear appropriate gloves. Barrier creams and water-based cleaners are also recommended.

Respiratory Protection

Check WHMIS labels and data sheets to determine whether respiratory protection must be worn with the products you are using.

Fire Protection

Because the flooring trades often work with flammable and explosive materials, always keep a fire extinguisher in the work area.

Ventilation is essential in preventing the accumulation of explosive gas, vapour, mist, and dust, especially in confined work areas. Sparks produced by tools can set off fires and explosions.

Refer to the protective measures in Chapter 5 HOUSEKEEPING and Chapter 15 CONFINED SPACES.

Tools

Specialized tools and equipment have been designed for the trade to reduce the risk of injury. Make every effort to avoid fatigue and long-term injury and health problems by using the proper equipment and following the procedures in this chapter.

Injuries resulting from continuous kneeling or bending during work can be reduced by using upright tools such as long-handled scrapers, rollers, and adhesive spray guns.

When using scrapers, wear hearing protection against high noise levels. Extensive vibration through the handles may be reduced by wearing thick gloves.

Long-Handled Scraper

Power Stretchers

Power stretchers are recommended whenever available and practical. Using the knee as a hammer may result in chronic knee problems.

Knee Kickers

Smaller and lighter than power stretchers, knee kickers are widely used by all carpet installers.

Replace damaged spikes and pads as soon as possible. Cotton heads should be cleaned regularly. Failure to do so can result in personal injury and material damage.

Knives

All knife-type tools can inflict serious cuts. These tools require careful handling, especially when stored in tool boxes or pouches.

Never hold your free hand in the direction of the cut.

Clear the area of loose obstructions and dangerous objects before installation. Many serious injuries have occurred when workers using knives have tripped, backed into, or fallen over objects in the work area.

Whenever possible, keep knives pointed in a safe direction and contained in holsters, scabbards, sheaths, or other protective cases when not in use.

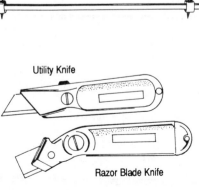

Power Stretcher

Knee Kickers

Scribing Tools

Utility Knife

Razor Blade Knife

Utility Knives — Equipped with a non-retractable spring steel blade, the knife should be handled carefully. Use caution when reaching for it in your tool pouch.

Razor Blade Knives — Extremely sharp, the fixed exposed blades have caused very serious cuts. Do not carelessly store in pouch, pocket, or toolbox.

Carpet-cutting Blades — Blades discarded or carelessly left lying around in remnants have caused many serious cuts.

Keep new and old blades in original or other suitable containers and dispose of them when practical.

Electric Staple Gun

These are quick, powerful fastening devices. They are not equipped with safety catches and will discharge when the trigger is depressed.

The gun can shoot staples with great force over a considerable distance. Never point the tool at anyone.

Disconnect power when cleaning, loading, or adjusting the gun.

Manual Staple Gun

The main hazard is injury to the eyes and hands.

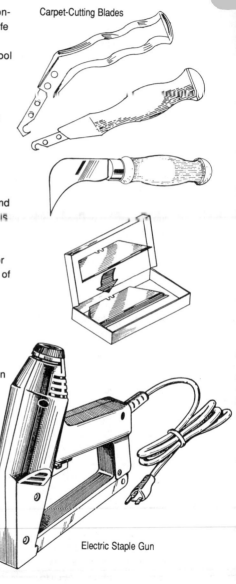

Carpet-Cutting Blades

Electric Staple Gun

Hot Air Gun

These are used for attaching seamless flooring. Capable of generating very high temperatures, the gun should be kept away from the skin.

Hammer Staplers

Always make sure the stapler is pointed in the right direction—down! Serious eye injuries have resulted when workers accidentally used the tool upside down. Remember—Tool may discharge staples when hit in either direction.

Spot Nailer and Mallet

Be careful and aim straight when striking head of nailer. Even a rubber mallet hurts if your hand is in the way.

Floor and Wall Scrapers

Scrapers are available in assorted lengths. Wherever possible, use one that allows you to work standing up.

Replacement steel blades are continuously exposed. Handling of these tools therefore requires care and concentration. To store in a toolbox or elsewhere, reverse the blade in its container.

Divider

Handle and store carefully to prevent stab injuries.

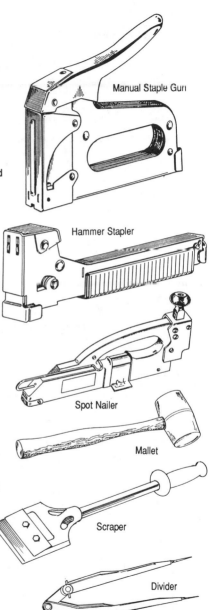

Manual Staple Gun

Hammer Stapler

Spot Nailer

Mallet

Scraper

Divider

Edge Trimmer

Be aware of the sharp hook end when using or storing this tool.

Knife and Tool Holster

Holsters are a good way to carry edged tools. Always remember to reach for tools carefully.

Four Wheel Dollies

These devices are extremely useful for moving heavy appliances and furniture and very effective in preventing injuries to back and damage to floor.

Back Care

Handling rolls of carpet and other flooring material presents major hazards in the trade.

Edge Trimmer

Holsters

Dollies

The sheer size and weight of the rolls that need to be handled and moved create the potential for back injuries.

Secure sheet vinyl rolls by tying off (if practical) or surround the rolls with pails of adhesive to keep them from toppling over.

Devices such as dollies, carts, and mechanical assists keep back injuries to a minimum and should be used whenever possible.

Before moving goods, inspect travel routes and destination. Determine the availability of material lifts and equipment. Check for areas needing special consideration or clean-up.

For more information, refer to Chapter 4 BACK CARE.

NOTES

NOTES

NOTES

NOTES